Manual 2

YOUNG WOMEN
Fun-tastic! Activities

You'll Find Activities to Match Lessons 1-49

❀ Young Women "Value-able" Journal and
❀ Lesson Match Activities to place in Journal
❀ Midweek Activities
❀ Scripture Cards

Gospel Subjects

Agency   Bishop   Blessings   Chastity   Choices   Commandments

Communication   Cooperation   Cultural Arts   Disabilities   Environment

Exaltation   Family History   Fasting   Finances   Gratitude   Homemaking

Honesty   Jesus Christ   Journals   Kingdom of God   Leadership   Life

Management   Missionary Work   Obedience   Optimism

Patriarchal Blessing   Patriotism   Peacemaker   Physical Health

Prayer   Priesthood   Revelation   Sacrament   Sacrifice

Self-Mastery   Spiritual Gifts   Talents   Temple Blessings

Temple Marriage   Testimony   Traditions   Work

Introducing the Author and Illustrator, Creators of the Following Series of Books and CD-ROMS:

Primary Partners® (manual match activities), *Sharing Time, Singing Fun,* and *Activity Days;*
Young Women Fun-tastic! Activities for Manuals 1-3 and
Young Women Fun-tastic! Personal Progress Motivators;
Gospel Fun Activities, Gospel Games, Super Singing Activities, Super Little Singers,
File Folder Family Home Evenings, and *Home-spun Fun Family Home Evenings*

Mary Ross, Author

Mary Ross is an energetic mother and has been a Primary teacher and Achievement Days leader. She loves to help children and young women have a good time while learning. She has studied acting, modeling, and voice. Her varied interests include writing, creating activities and children's parties, and cooking. Mary and her husband, Paul, live with their daughter, Jennifer, in Sandy, Utah.

Jennette Guymon-King, Illustrator

Jennette Guymon-King studied graphic arts and illustration at Utah Valley College and the University of Utah. She served a mission in Japan. Jennette enjoys sports, reading, cooking, art, gardening, and freelance illustrating. Jennette and her husband, Clayton, live in Riverton, Utah. They are the proud parents of their daughter Kayla Mae, and sons Levi and Carson.

Covenant Communications, Inc.
American Fork, Utah

Printed in Canada
First Printing: September 1999

Young Women FUN-TASTIC! Activities - Manual 2
ISBN 1-57734-687-4

Acknowledge: Thanks to Inspire Graphics (www.inspiregraphics.com) for the Lettering Delights fonts.

My Young Women
Value-able Journal

photo

I will bloom
where I'm planted.

"Thou shalt be like a watered garden."
Isaiah 58:11

INTRODUCTION
Fun-tastic! Young Women Activities
Lesson Lifesavers and More for Manual 2*

You'll find the following activities
to match lessons 1-49 to help young women
"Bloom where they are planted":

❀ Lesson Activities   ❀ Midweek Activities

❀ Scripture Cards   ❀ Young Women "Value-able" Journal with
Seven value dividers to store activities

❀ **TO COLOR OR COPY IMAGES:** You will also find this book on
CD-ROM. You can print images instantly from your home
computer in full color or black and white. Just ask for the *Young
Women Fun-tastic! Activities, Manual 2* CD-ROM (shown right).

HOW TO USE THIS BOOK
❀ **Lessons 1-49 Table of Contents** helps you locate activities by
the lesson numbers.
❀ **A-Z Table of Contents** helps you locate activities by subject.
❀ **Lesson Activities** coordinate with specific parts of the lesson
(for example, lesson 18, My Righteous Traditions Time Capsule
complements page 65 in the *Young Women manual* (see the
PREPARATION section for each activity).
❀ **Midweek Activities** enhance your lessons with a lesson and
follow-up activity during the next week. This keeps the subject
open for discussion, giving more meaning to the lesson taught on
Sunday. Many of the midweek activities in this book were
contributed by Fern Law, a Young Women leader of six years.
Note: Use only the first 10-15 minutes of your midweek activity
to review the matching lesson. Many of the midweek activity ideas
can take up the entire evening.

I want to develop...
Righteous Traditions
...now and pass them on to my family.
The righteous habits I want to acquire are:

My Righteous Traditions
Time Capsule
Date sealed
Date to be opened

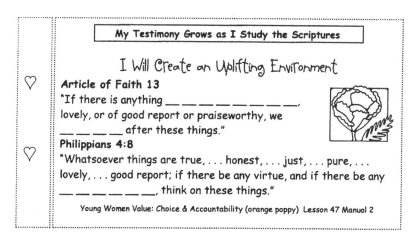

My Testimony Grows as I Study the Scriptures

I Will Create an Uplifting Environment

♡ **Article of Faith 13**
"If there is anything _ _ _ _ _ _ _ _ _ _ _ _,
lovely, or of good report or praiseworthy, we
_ _ _ _ _ _ after these things."

♡ **Philippians 4:8**
"Whatsoever things are true, . . . honest, . . . just, . . . pure, . . .
lovely, . . . good report; if there be any virtue, and if there be any
_ _ _ _ _ _ _ _, think on these things."

Young Women Value: Choice & Accountability (orange poppy) Lesson 47 Manual 2

❀ **Scripture Cards** (pages
116-132, shown left)
encourage young women to
learn a "value-able"
scripture each week. Fill in
the missing words, and color the floral
symbol (shown below and left).

Young Women Manual 2 is published by The Church of Jesus Christ of Latter-day Saints, Salt Lake City, Utah.

ORGANIZE JOURNAL

1. Create Value Dividers by selecting a three-ring binder for each young woman and copying the value cover pages and value tabs (found in the back of this book). Follow the instructions to set up divider tabs.

2. Identify the Floral Symbols above found on the activities and scripture cards. They will help young women identify the values: *Faith* (white lily), *Divine Nature* (blue morning glory), *Individual Worth* (red rose), *Knowledge* (green ivy), *Choice and Accountability* (orange poppy), *Good Works* (yellow sunflower), and *Integrity* (purple pansy).

3. Color Code the Journal by coloring the floral symbol found on most of the activities (see the *Individual Worth* red rose symbol, shown on the journal page on the left and activity on the right). Place the activity in the journal binder behind the value tab. Encourage young women to post the activity on a wall or mirror to review during the week before placing it in their journal.

4. Create Divider Pockets to place odd-sized activities by mounting an 8 ½ x 5-inch piece of cardstock on the back of the value divider page.

❀ **Evening of Excellence** is a great time for young women to display their Young Women Value-able Journal. Each week they can collect activities and handouts and store them in their journal. Parents will delight in their daughters' grasp of gospel subjects. Young women can also display their scrapbooks and the journal (described above).

❀ **Personal Progress Motivators:** Don't miss the new *Young Women Fun-tastic! Personal Progress Motivators* book and CD-ROM (shown right). Now you can encourage young women with seven midweek activities to spotlight each value. Each includes an invitation, a certificate, rewarding activities, a Value Quilt with quilt blocks young women can earn after completing each value's goals, and more.

❀ **Manuals 1 and 3 Activities:** Look for more activities in the *Young Women Fun-tastic!* books and CD-ROMs to add to and enhance your lessons.

Table of Contents

- A-Z Preview of Lesson Activities (1-49 of *Young Women Manual* 2*)
- Young Women Value-able Journal (Dividers and Tabs)

*Young Women Manual 2 is published by The Church of Jesus Christ of Latter-day Saints, Salt Lake City, Utah.

Young Women Manual 2 is published by The Church of Jesus Christ of Latter-day Saints, Salt Lake City, Utah.

28—**AGENCY:** I Have the Freedom to Choose (Consequences Quiz), 67-68

11—**BISHOP** Appreciation (Thanks a Bunch! Sunflowers in a Pot), 26-28

12—**BLESSINGS** from Heavenly Father (Special Blessing Journal), 29-30

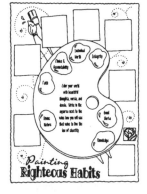

37—**CHASTITY:** Painting Righteous Habits (Planner), 88-89

33—**CHASTITY** (It's a Jungle Out There Quicksand Puzzle), 79-81

35—**CHOICES:** Wise Choices (Thumbs Up/Down Choices Game), 84-85

4—**COMMANDMENTS:** Divine Roles (Commandments Opposites Game), 8-10

8—**COMMUNICATION:** (Soar High Family Balloon Bouquet), 18-20

7—**COOPERATION:** Harmony at Home (Love at Home Spin-the-Bottle), 15-17

45—**CULTURAL ARTS:** (I Love the Cultural Arts! Frame/Journal), 106-107

49—**DISABILITIES:** Encourage Others (Sunny Action Planner), 115-116

47—**ENVIRONMENT:** Uplift (It's Time for a Change! Diaper Bag), 110-112

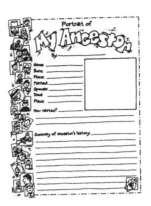

29—EXALTATION: (Premortal, Earth Life, Exaltation Mobile), 69-72

17—FAMILY HISTORY: Family History (Portrait of Ancestor), 43-44

23—FASTING: (Fasting PIZZA! Doorknob Fasting Reminder), 55-56

46—FINANCES: Responsible (Money Mottos to Place in Wallet), 108-109

42—GRATITUDE: (Gratitude Card and Grateful Heart! Bookmark), 98-100

5—HOMEMAKING: (Home "Tweet" Home Improvement List), 11-12

36—HONESTY: (I'm "Sew" Honest! Stand-up Card), 86-87

1—JESUS CHRIST: Close to Savior (Life Preserver Promises Poster), 1-2

16—JOURNALS: Record the History of My Life (Journal Pages), 38-42

3—KINGDOM OF GOD: Build Kingdom (Jewels in My Crown Service List), 6-7

48—LEADERSHIP Skills (A Loving or Lazy Leader Word Find), 113-114

32—LIFE Is Sacred (Life Is Sacred! Lullaby Lollipop), 77-78

43—**MANAGEMENT:** Time Use (My Ant Farm Leisure Time Log), 101-102

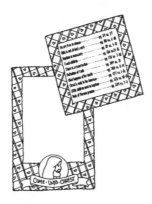

20—**MISSIONARY** (Book of Mormon Testimony & Underlining), 49-50

21—**MISSIONARY** Letter Writing (Do and Don't List and Postcard), 51-52

19—**MISSIONARY WORK:** Prepare (Missionary Prep Motivators), 47-48

34—**OBEDIENCE:** Standards (Hold Fast Word Find), 82-83

41—**OPTIMISM:** Cheerful Attitude (Cup Full of Cheerful Thoughts), 96-97

13—**PATRIARCHAL BLESSING** (Prep Checklist and Message Memo), 31-33

31—**PATRIOTISM** (I Love My Country! Community Service Find), 75-76

9—**PEACEMAKER:** (Home Is Heavenly Peacemaker Tent Card), 21-22

39—**PHYSICAL HEALTH** (Be Free of Disease! Unseen Fiend Find), 92-93

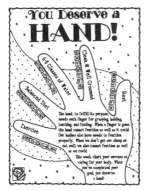

38—**PHYSICAL HEALTH:** (You Deserve a HAND! Health Chart), 90-91

22—**PRAYER:** Counsel with the Lord (Tent Card/Prayer Chart), 53-54

10—**PRIESTHOOD:** (Priesthood Power Blessings Journal), 23-25

24—**REVELATION:** (Candle of the Lord Scripture Wordsearch), 57-58

26—**SACRAMENT:** I Will Choose the Right (Sacrament Thought Card), 61-62

25—**SACRIFICE:** (Something to Sacrifice Goal Planner), 59-60

40—**SELF-MASTERY:** Character (Harvesting My Destiny Garden), 94-95

2—**SPIRITUAL GIFTS:** (Spiritual Gifts Writing and Match Game), 3-5

44—**TALENTS:** (My Basket Full of Talents! Talented Egg Show), 103-105

14—**TEMPLE BLESSINGS** (Value List to Earn Temple Blessings), 34-35

15—**TEMPLE MARRIAGE** Preparation (Temple Preparation Tent Card), 36-37

27—**TESTIMONY** (Lost & Found Game) 63; 30—(Gifts Service Plan), 73-74

18—**TRADITIONS** (My Righteous Traditions Time Capsule), 45-46

6—**WORK:** Sharing (Home "Tweet" Home No-Mess Nest Routine), 13-14

Lesson 1 — *Jesus Christ: I Will Draw Close to My Savior*
(Life Preserver Promise Poster)

I can successfully sail the seas of life because...

.. Jesus is my life-Savior

Draw closer to Jesus Christ by making three life preserver promises. Post and read them each day as a reminder.

Prayer

Scriptures

Motions

PREPARATION: Review scripture and discussion (p. 3) in *Young Women Manual 2.*

TO MAKE ACTIVITY HANDOUT: *Copy and color *Life Preserver Poster* (p. 2) for each young woman.

LESSON MATCH ACTIVITY—*Life Preserver Promise Poster:*

1. Read D&C 88:63 and tell young women, "You can be successful as you sail the seas of life because Jesus is our life-Savior. Because of His divine sacrifice in giving His life for us, we can live again. If we keep the promises found in this poster activity, we can develop a greater testimony of our Savior and feel closer to Him day to day.

2. Have young women write on the handout three life-preserver promises they want to keep and have them post it to read daily.

COLOR FLORAL SYMBOL:

*Color floral symbol on activity and scripture card. File activity in Young Women "Value-able" Journal behind the value tab.

Divine Nature (blue morning glory)

MIDWEEK ACTIVITIES:

Review Books and Articles about Jesus:
Review those written by the living Prophet or General Authorities. Assign parts of the book or article to each young woman to summarize, sharing thoughts. Invite discussion.

Walk and Talk Where Jesus Walked:
Create a reverent ambience where young women walk on footprints that lead to pictures and stories about the life of Jesus. As much as possible, create a setting reminiscent of Jerusalem. Learn about the customs and traditions of the Jews. Tell about the conditions and political climate. Include music.

Have a Bread-Baking Contest:
Share samples of food Jesus would have eaten like unleavened bread (without yeast), milk, and honey. Also have bread dough (raised, using yeast) for young women to design shapes. Bake, vote, and give awards, e.g. "Most Creative," "Funniest," "Most Likely to Be Eaten First," etc. Have quotes to hand out or enlarged to read:

*"Come unto me . . . buy milk and honey,
without money."* (2 Nephi 26:25)
*"Man cannot live by bread alone, but by every word
that proceedeth out of the mouth of God."*
(Matthew 4:4)

Paint a Prayer Rock:
Provide a medium-sized rock and paints for young women to paint their own personal rock. Using the scriptures, talk about prayer. Invite leaders and young women to share their experiences and testimonies on prayer. Have young women place prayer rock under, or on, their pillow to remind them to pray before going to bed. Tell them: "If you bump your head, then there are prayers to be said."

I can successfully sail the seas of life because...

...Jesus is my life-Savior.

Draw closer to Jesus Christ by making three life preserver promises. Post and read them each day as a reminder.

Prayer

Scriptures

Actions

Lesson 2 Spiritual Gifts: Spiritual Gifts Help Me Gain Eternal Life
(Spiritual Gifts Writing Activity and Match Game)

PREPARATION: Review object lesson and discussion and chalkboard discussion (p. 5) in *Young Women Manual 2.*

TO MAKE ACTIVITY HANDOUT: *Copy, color, and cut out the *Spiritual Gifts* envelope and cards (p. 4-5) for each young woman. Fold the tabs and glue envelope together leaving the top flap open. Insert gift cards inside.

LESSON MATCH ACTIVITY—*Spiritual Gifts Writing Activity and Match Game:*
1. Tell young women there are two different kinds of gifts, tangible and intangible. Tangible gifts that come wrapped up in a package are nice, but they do not last long. If we focus on these gifts too much, we will become a small package and our lives will be shallow and empty. By spending too much time on our tangible or physical possessions, we neglect our spiritual or intangible side.
2. Read D&C 46:8-9: *"Seek ye earnestly the best gifts . . . for they are given for the benefit of those who love me and keep all my commandments."* Also Timothy 4:14: *"Neglect not the gift that is within thee."*
3. Read instructions on the envelope to find lasting gifts.
4. Have young women list on the envelope ways they can focus on spiritual gifts (for example, read scriptures, Church books, and magazines; attend Church meetings; listen to LDS motivational tapes and music; turn off the TV; ask for a blessing when sick or in need; ask for spiritual gifts; pray).
5. Play a match game with the gift cards. If using several sets of cards, have young women place their initials on back of cards to retrieve later.

COLOR SYMBOL: *Color floral symbol on activity and scripture card. File activity in Young Women "Value-able" Journal behind the value tab.

Individual Worth (red rose)

MIDWEEK ACTIVITIES:
Spiritual Gifts Box: Create a Spiritual Gifts Box that young women can cherish and use to remember their spiritual gifts. Ask young women to take small slips of paper and write on them special talents, gifts, and positive character traits they see in each young woman. If there are ten young women, they should all receive nine notes for their box, plus notes from leaders. Ask young women not to talk during this time so girls can feel inspired as they write. Open and close activity with prayer.
Exchange Spiritual Gifts: A week ahead, have young women draw names to exchange gifts the following week. Have them thoughtfully select an item that represents a spiritual gift Heavenly Father has given that young woman. Write a note about the gift, exchange gifts, and read the note aloud. *Ideas:* A magnet could represent a "magnetic" personality; a plum could say she is "plum" nice; a jug of water (a pure heart and mind); a bolt (she's like a "bolt" of lightning—fun to be around); a diaper pin (she's good with children); a picture of Jesus (she follows in His steps); picture or poem describing this person; a handkerchief (enjoy her testimony).

*All images can be printed in color or black and white using the *Young Women Fun-tastic! Activities—Manual 2* CD-ROM.

...are lasting
and
eternal.

Spiritual Gifts

Look inside this package to find spiritual gifts. Using the reference on each card, determine the gift and fill in the blank.
Then think of ways you can focus on and improve your spiritual gifts and write them below:

Ways I will focus on my spiritual gifts:

_____

_____

_____

_____

_____

1 Timothy 4:14

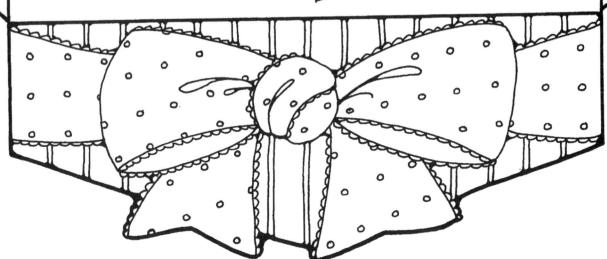

Lesson 3 | Kingdom of God: I Will Build God's Kingdom
(Jewels in My Crown Service List)

PREPARATION: Review lesson applications 1-3 (p. 12) in *Young Women Manual 2*.

TO MAKE ACTIVITY HANDOUT: *Copy and color the *Jewels in My Crown Service List* (p. 7) for each young woman.

LESSON MATCH ACTIVITY—*Jewels in My Crown Service List*:

1. Explain to young women that service can be their crowning glory. By giving of their time, talents, and possessions, they will be rewarded with blessings here and eternally.

2. Read Matthew 6:33: *"Seek ye first the kingdom of God, and his righteousness; and all these things shall be added unto you."*

3. Have young women list on the handout ways they will personally give of their time, talents, and possessions to build up the kingdom of God. Ideas are found in the border.

Note: See Lesson 29 (p. 69) Midweek Activity "Jewels in My Crown Service Project."

COLOR FLORAL SYMBOL:

*Color floral symbol on activity and scripture card. File activity in Young Women "Value-able" Journal behind the value tab.

Divine Nature (blue morning glory)

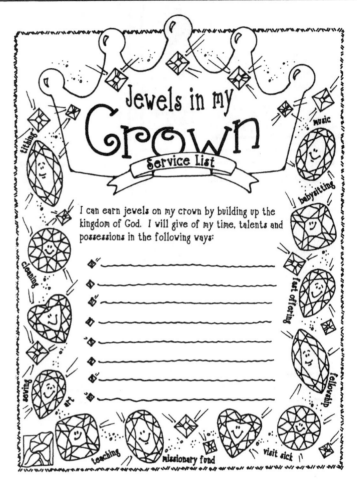

MIDWEEK ACTIVITIES:

Kidnap (Invite) and Fellowship a Less-Active Young Woman:
With permission of the girl's parents, take a less-active class member out for pizza, bowling, or something she likes to do.

Invite-a-Friend Activity:
This is a great way for young women to include a less-active young woman or friend of another faith. Have a barbeque or indoor picnic, play volleyball, baseball, frisbee football, basketball, or other interactive games.

Have a Talent Show:
This way young women can share in skits, sing-alongs or lip syncs, poetry reading, piano recitals, arts and crafts exhibits, and more.

Have a *Crazy Mixed-up Fashion Show:
Young women can model something from a "Crazy Mixed-up Grab Bag" or bags filled with five or six weird outfits. Have young women make up scripts and put on skits to match the wardrobe in their group's bag.

Service Brainstorm:
Young women and leaders can divide into two teams. Have each invent ten fun ways to be of service. Have a panel of three judges score each idea.

Jewels in my Crown

Service List

I can earn jewels on my crown by building up the kingdom of God. I will give of my time, talents and possessions in the following ways:

_____
_____
_____
_____
_____
_____
_____
_____

tithing

music

babysitting

cleaning

fast offering

sewing

art

fellowship

teaching

missionary fund

visit sick

Lesson 4 | **Commandments: Commandments Help Me Fulfill Divine Roles**
(Commandment Opposites Match Game)

PREPARATION: Review activity (p. 14, referring to handout on page 17) in Young Women Manual 2*.

TO MAKE ACTIVITY HANDOUT: *Copy and cut out the *Commandment Opposites* broken and kept commandment cards (p. 10) for each young woman.

LESSON MATCH ACTIVITY—*Commandment Opposites Match Game*: By playing this match game young women can gain a better understanding how commandments are broken and kept and learn how this could prevent or help them fulfill their divine roles.

To Play:

1. Lay cards facedown on a flat surface.

2. Take turns turning cards over to make an opposites match (e.g., "Jealousy, envy, greed" matches with "Do not covet"). When a match is made, have the young woman tell specific things she can do to obey this commandment (e.g., examples of "let virtue garnish thy thoughts unceasingly" could be "watch only G and PG movies, play worthy music, hum a hymn when I think a bad thought").

3. Talk about how each action might affect their abilities to fulfil their divine roles.

4. Play until all matches are made. The person or team with the most matched cards wins!

Note: The matching cards are in the same position on the second page.

COLOR FLORAL SYMBOL:

*Color floral symbol on activity and scripture card. File activity in Young Women "Value-able" Journal behind the value tab.

> *Divine Nature (blue morning glory)*

MIDWEEK ACTIVITY:

Obedience Bonfire: Have a canyon or backyard bonfire (or create a bonfire scene with paper fire and rocks to look like a bonfire and place indoors). Have a special speaker (bishop, seminary teacher, member of stake presidency, etc.). Speak on commandments and why it is important to obey the commandments. Have each young woman write an action she would like to change on a small piece of paper and then toss it into the fire. Talk about letting go of our sins or weaknesses. Roast marshmallows and make s'mores over the fire. If having indoors, prepare ahead, melting marshmallows in the oven.

---

*All images can be printed in color or black and white using the *Young Women Fun-tastic! Activities—Manual 2* CD-ROM.

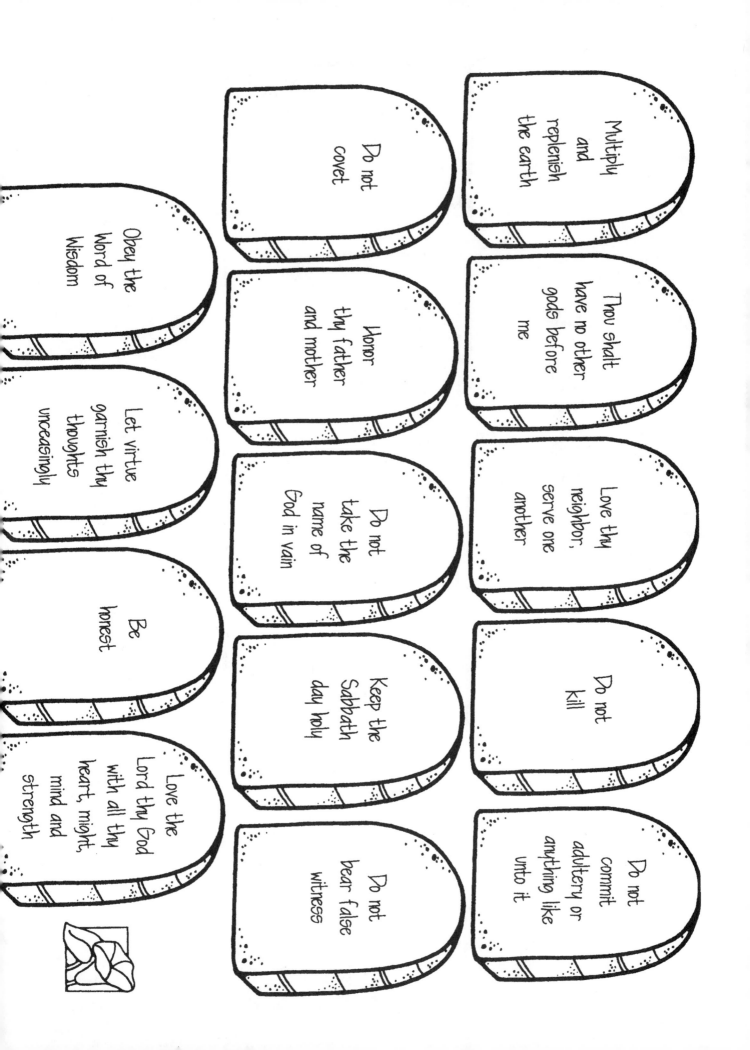

Multiply and replenish the earth

Do not covet

Obey the Word of Wisdom

Thou shalt have no other gods before me

Honor thy father and mother

Let virtue garnish thy thoughts unceasingly

Love thy neighbor, serve one another

Do not take the name of God in vain

Be honest

Do not kill

Keep the Sabbath day holy

Love the Lord thy God with all thy heart, might, mind and strength

Do not bear false witness

Do not commit adultery or anything like unto it

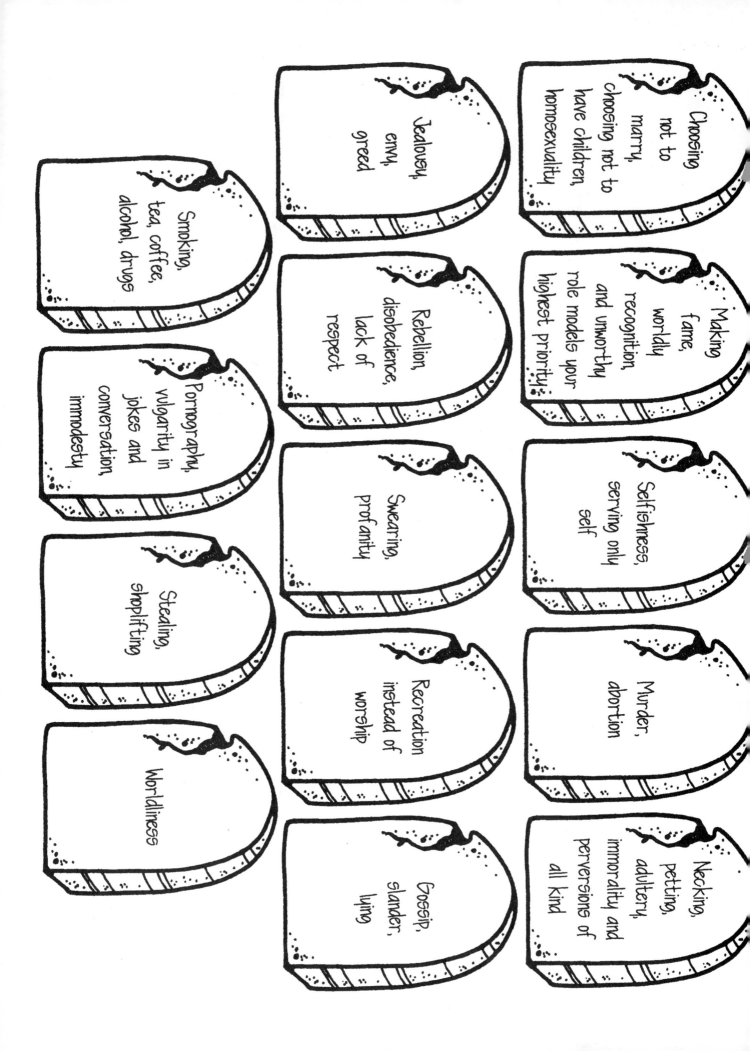

Choosing not to marry, choosing not to have children, homosexuality

Jealousy, envy, greed

Smoking, tea, coffee, alcohol, drugs

Making fame, worldly recognition, and unworthy role models your highest priority

Rebellion, disobedience, lack of respect

Pornography, vulgarity in jokes and conversation, immodesty

Selfishness, serving only self

Swearing, profanity

Stealing, shoplifting

Murder, abortion

Recreation instead of worship

Worldliness

Necking, petting, adultery, immorality and perversions of all kind

Gossip, slander, lying

Lesson 5	Homemaking: Home Can Be a Special Place
	(Home "Tweet" Home Improvement List)

PREPARATION: Review activity (p. 19) in *Young Women Manual 2*.

TO MAKE ACTIVITY HANDOUT: *Copy, color, and cut out a *Home "Tweet" Home Improvement List* for each young woman.

LESSON MATCH ACTIVITY—*Home "Tweet" Home Improvement List*: Help young women identify things they can do outside of everyday tasks that will make home a more pleasant place to be.

1. Using the handout, have young women make a list of things they can do anytime to improve their environment at home.

2. Challenge them to go to the list whenever they have free or leisure time, and work on the tasks to make home a "tweet" (sweet) place to be. List odd jobs that don't normally get done everyday to improve life at home (e.g., clean out a drawer, cupboard, closet, or a corner in the garage or basement).

Note: This *Home "Tweet" Home Improvement List* is different from the Home "Tweet" Home No-Mess Nest Routine (see Lesson 6), where you list daily tasks, e.g., shine the bathroom counter, make your bed.

COLOR FLORAL SYMBOL:

*Color floral symbol on activity and scripture card. File activity in Young Women "Value-able" Journal behind the value tab.

Good Works (yellow sunflower)

MIDWEEK ACTIVITIES:

Mock Bedroom Cleanup:

Have someone come and show young women how to clean their room. Have a mock bedroom set up or visit a young woman's room (make arrangements ahead of time). Talk about how the room looks (being careful not to offend) and how it reflects on how they feel. Personal grooming and attitude is often reflected in how well the room is kept.

Old-Fashioned and Modern Housekeeping:

Ask an older sister to tell young women what it was like cleaning in her grandmother's day, when she was the age of the young women. She could tell how women used a ringer washer or hung the clothes on the line instead of the washer and dryer of today. Or, how they rubbed hand soap into the stain or used a washboard instead of spray-and-wash or the other spot and stain removers of today.

Bird House Cleanup or Pet Grooming:

Pets need cleaning too. Borrow someone's pet bird and demonstrate how to clean out a bird cage and care for a bird. Or you might show how to give a dog a bath and/or cut their hair. Cats keep themselves clean, but they need to have their teeth cleaned regularly by a vet.

Pretzel Party:

Show how to make pretzels or fun-shaped rolls. Contact the Rhodes Company for a free booklet or demonstration.

Lesson 6	Work: Work Is Easier If We All Share
	(Home "Tweet" Home No-Mess Nest Routine)

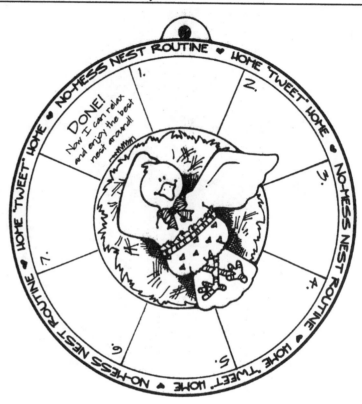

PREPARATION: Review lesson application (p. 24) in *Young Women Manual 2*.

TO MAKE ACTIVITY HANDOUT: *Copy, color, and cut out a *Home "Tweet" No-Mess Nest Routine* parts A and B (p. 14) for each young woman. Attach bird arrow on top of wheel with a paper fastener.

LESSON MATCH ACTIVITY—*Home "Tweet" Home No-Mess Nest Routine*: Help young women identify things they can do on a daily and weekly basis that will help make their home a more pleasant place to be.
1. Have young women write on the wheel tasks they plan to complete each day.
2. Challenge them to do these each day and week to make the chores a habit.
Examples: (1) Don't leave a room without putting at least three things away; (2) Shine the bathroom counter and mirrors each night; (3) Wash, iron, and care for clothing; (4) Do the dinner or breakfast dishes; (5) Put away clutter in one or more rooms; (6) Prepare a meal and clean up the mess. *Note:* This *Home "Tweet" Home No-Mess Nest Routine* is different from the Home "Tweet" Home Improvement List (see Lesson 5), where you list odd jobs you don't have to do each day that make a great improvement, e.g., clean out a drawer, cupboard, closet, or a corner in the garage or basement.

COLOR FLORAL SYMBOL:
*Color floral symbol on scripture card. File activity in Young Women "Value-able" Journal behind the value tab.

Good Works (yellow sunflower)

MIDWEEK ACTIVITIES:

Job Jar and Job Jar General:
Help young women create their own "Job Jar" label to place on a jar with job wordstrips to place inside. Have them work with their family, with a Job General in charge for the week, and have each person draw a job from the jar, tell the General the job, and report back to the Job General when the job is complete.

Timer Tactics:
Have young women go through a home with a timer in hand. Divide into pairs and assign a room, giving 5-10 minutes per room. Ask them to beat the clock and clean the room before the timer rings. With two working together, it makes work enjoyable and they can get twice as much done.

Closet Concentration:
Tell young women that next week they are going to have a closet tour to get ready for inspection and to offer ideas on how to keep a closet clean. If they are not ready for the closet tour, others can come and help. *Ideas:* (1) Hang clothes in groups of colors or items, e.g., pants with pants, shirts with shirts. (2) Place empty hangers in two different boxes or shelves so they are handy for quick hang-ups. (3) Put everything in its place, e.g., fold clothes in drawers and keep items of their kind separated. (4) Simplify wardrobe by not keeping items you don't wear.

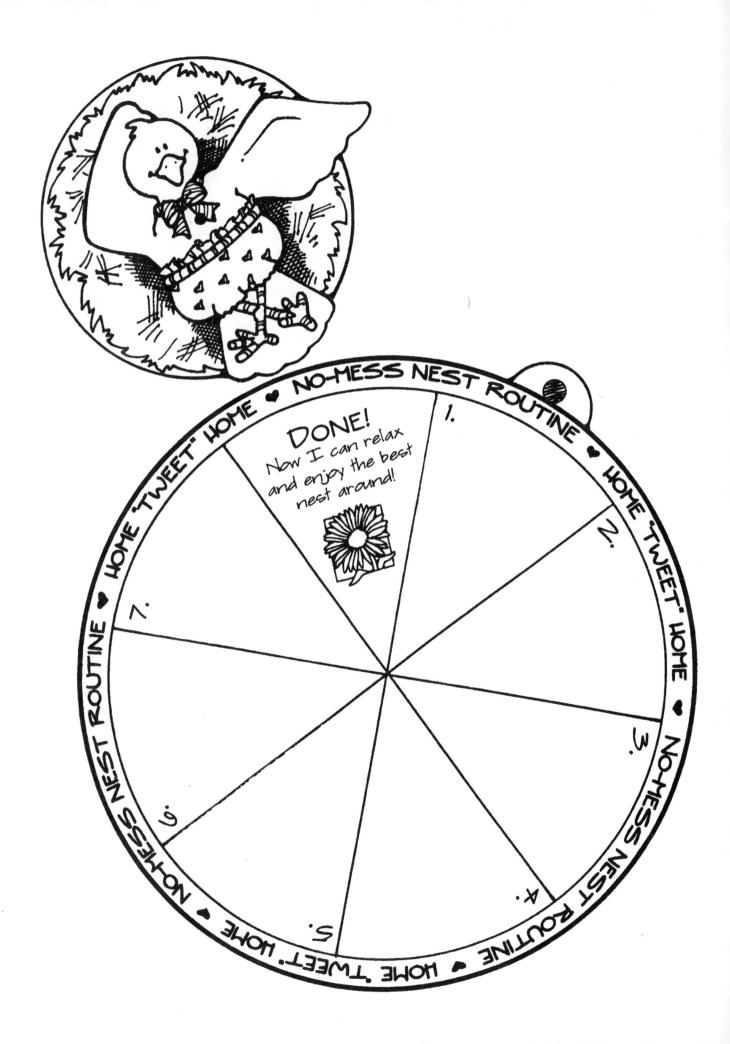

NO-MESS NEST ROUTINE ♥ HOME "TWEET" HOME ♥ NO-MESS NEST ROUTINE ♥ HOME "TWEET" HOME ♥ NO-MESS NEST ROUTINE ♥ HOME "TWEET" HOME ♥

DONE!
Now I can relax
and enjoy the best
nest around!

1.

2.

3.

4.

5.

6.

7.

Lesson 7	Cooperation: I Will Create Love and Harmony at Home
	(Love at Home Spin-the-Bottle)

PREPARATION: Review case studies 1-8 (p. 26-27) in *Young Women Manual 2.*

TO MAKE ACTIVITY HANDOUT: *Copy, color, and cut out the *Love at Home* jar label and wordstrips (p. 16-17) for each young woman. Place label on a jar and wordstrips inside jar. They can make up more situations that may fit their family, then write them down and place them in the bottle.

LESSON MATCH ACTIVITY—*Love at Home Spin-the-Bottle*: Help young women tell how they would show love in each situation. Have them take this home to share with their family. *To Play:* Read the game rules found on the bottle (p. 16) aloud and play.

COLOR FLORAL SYMBOL:
*Color floral symbol on activity and scripture card. File activity in Young Women "Value-able" Journal behind the value tab.

Good Works (yellow sunflower)

It's a holiday and you are out of school. You are so relieved that you don't have homework. You plant yourself on the couch and ask your self to fix you breakfast, lunch,

Your favorite TV show is on and your homework is not done. You promised your parents you will study after the show is over. ...st friend comes over.

Your best friend comes over. Your mother asks you to take out the garbage, clean up your mess, and straighten your room.

MIDWEEK ACTIVITIES:

Harmony in the Home Panel:
Have the bishop and his counselors and their wives do a panel discussion on harmony in their homes. Have each young woman write a question or two for discussion. You could ask the stake presidency and wives to come also.

Peacemaker Hints:
Have someone come and talk about ways to bring peace in the home. *Ideas:* Learning relaxation techniques; creating peace when there is conflict; creating cooperation in the home; creating love when conflict comes; planning for and fixing meals ahead so that family members can eat on time; feeding the family spiritually; having scripture study, family home evening, and family counsel; planning family activities that bring peace and love; and sharing tasks.

TO PLAY LOVE AT HOME SPIN-THE-BOTTLE:
Sit in a circle and spin the bottle. When the bottleneck points to you, read a wordstrip and tell how you would show love in that situation. If you have responded to two situations already, choose someone else who hasn't had a turn.

	Your best friend comes over. Your mother asks you to take out the garbage, clean up your mess, and straighten your room.		Your family reunion is next week, the same time you and your friends planned a trip to the amusement park.
	You leave your room each day with the bed unmade and clothes on the bed. You say that you don't have time and you'll do it after school. After school you're very busy again.		You spill food on your shirt and can't find the stain remover so you leave it. When the stain won't come out, you ask your mother to buy you another shirt.
	Your favorite TV show is on and your homework is not done. You promised your parents you would study after the show is over. But then your best friend comes over.		Your grandparents find it hard to do certain chores like cooking meals and doing the dishes. Grandpa has arthritis and can't get to the cobwebs and you see spiders around the house.
	You have permission to go with your friends if you call home when you get to the activity. Your mother can't concentrate on the lesson she is preparing because she hasn't heard from you.		You and your brother haven't been getting along. The problem is, he's good in math and you have a math quiz coming up and you could use some help.
	It's a holiday and you are out of school. You are so relieved that you don't have homework. You plant yourself on the couch and ask your mother to fix you breakfast, lunch, and dinner.		Your sister is sick. You are starting to feel sick, too. There is no one around to help.

You're so tired of your science teacher giving you homework, and you don't really like his personality or the way he teaches. You listen to your friends complain about this and are tempted to do the same.	Your parents ask you not to study on Sunday. When the weekend comes you have a lot of homework but you're so tired of school. You call your friends and fill your calendar with activities Friday and Saturday. Sunday comes and the homework isn't done.
You wouldn't mind washing the dishes if you just didn't have so many other things to do. When the meals are over, you leave your plate on the table and work on homework or relax.	The dog is out most of the day now and it's getting hotter. You are thirsty, but you don't even think about the dog needing a drink—out of sight, out of mind.
You can see that your mother has worked all day shopping and preparing the meals. You like what she made for dinner but you are too busy telling her about your day to notice.	Your little sister likes to play with her little people toys. She keeps asking you to play with her and you tell her you will. But lately you're so busy that she plays alone.
Your little brother stutters and has a hard time forming words. He needs someone to help him read but you are not interested in reading children's books.	Your older brother is going on a mission. One day you see that he is thinking about his family and how much he will miss them when he is gone.
You're almost 16 and you want to drive the car. Your parents are concerned about you driving alone. You tell your friend that you'll pick her up. The car is outside but no one else is home.	Last weekend you were too busy to help around the house. The clutter is piling up, the floors are unswept, and the bathrooms need cleaning, but you have tons of homework.
Your grandmother lives with you and everyone tells her they love her when they see her, but lately she hasn't had a lot of visits and she misses her late husband.	It's Christmas and Dad says the money is tight. You have a limited amount of cash but you do know how to sew.
Your dad keeps asking you if you're happy. He likes to see you smile but you're preoccupied, worrying about your homework, piano recital, and getting your room cleaned.	Cooking is not something you know a lot about. You would like to come home from school to something good to eat, but your mother works and you and your sister come home alone.

Lesson 8 — Communication: I Will Communicate with My Family
(Soar High! Family Communication Balloon Bouquet)

PREPARATION: Review handout (p. 31-32) in *Young Women Manual 2.*

TO MAKE ACTIVITY HANDOUT: *Copy, color, and cut out eight balloons (p. 19-20), eight 12-inch pieces of colored string, yarn, or ribbon for each young woman. Tape a 12-inch string or ribbon to the back or tie to each balloon. Double-stick tape the *Soar High!* cloud and balloons to a poster, door, or wall. Gather all strings together and tie to make a bouquet.

LESSON MATCH ACTIVITY—*Soar High! Family Communication Balloon Bouquet:* Help young women learn eight ways they can improve their family communication. Make and display a balloon bouquet in class. Have young women make one to share with their family and display in their room.

COLOR FLORAL SYMBOL:
*Color floral symbol on activity and scripture card. File activity in Young Women "Value-able" Journal behind the value tab.

> *Good Works (yellow sunflower)*

MIDWEEK ACTIVITIES:
Compare Lasting Family Relationships with Fading Friends:

Talk about getting along with your family now because family relationships are those that last. Bring pictures from your childhood (e.g., you in kindergarten, grade school, junior high, high school, your best friend in high school, or college, your boyfriends). As you show them, you might say, "I'm not as close to them now as I once was. The people who really matter now are my family, but at the time I gave up spending time with them to be in these short-term relationships." Give young women some time and stationery to write a long overdue note of appreciation to a family member.

Evening of Soar High! Communication Techniques:
Have training on proper introductions, etiquette, and appropriate behavior (e.g., when to speak and not to speak). Have quotes and scriptures on communication (see James 1:26 and 3:5-6). Finish by playing Charades with phrases that go along with the lesson or some other similar game. (For example, Brigham Young said, *"You cannot hide the heart when the mouth is open").*

Family Communication Speaker(s):
Have someone talk about family communication. Look for someone who has a large family or someone the Relief Society or bishopric recommends. Find quotes from a family relations class that are appropriate and have the young women take turns sharing them. You could also have a panel of two families and ask them questions.

Learn to Write:
Learn the art of writing letters, thank-you notes, making personalized cards, and organizing correspondence. Ask young women to create a card for each month and to schedule birthdays, anniversaries, holidays, and other special days to remind them to send letters or cards.

Lesson 9	Peacemaker: I Will Be a Peacemaker in My Home
	(Home Is Heavenly! Peacemaker Tent Card)

PREPARATION: Review handout (p. 31-32) in *Young Women Manual 2.*

TO MAKE ACTIVITY HANDOUT: *Copy, color, cut out, and fold the *Home Is Heavenly Peacemaker Tent Card* (p. 22) on cardstock paper for each young woman.

LESSON MATCH ACTIVITY—*Home Is Heavenly Peacemaker Tent Card:*

1. Ask young women to take this home and share with their family, asking for help in making their home a peaceful place to live.

2. In class divide young women into five groups, pairing off in two or more to talk privately about how each can be a peacemaker in these five areas (shown on the tent card, e.g., "I am a peacemaker because I show love and understanding"). Assign each group one of these areas to report on. Give each group five minutes and ask each young woman to report how she plans to use this idea to be a peacemaker (e.g., "I will listen to my brother as he tells me about his day").

COLOR FLORAL SYMBOL:

*Color floral symbol on activity and scripture card. File activity in Young Women "Value-able" Journal behind the value tab.

Good Works (yellow sunflower)

MIDWEEK ACTIVITIES:

Peaceful Puzzle:

Encourage young women to think about developing peace within as they create a puzzle with pictures drawn of peaceful actions, or as they read the following quotes to remind them to develop good habits that bring feelings of peace. *"The chains of habit are generally too small to be felt until they are too strong to be broken"* (Samuel Johnson). *"Better keep yourself clean and bright; you are the window through which you must see the world"* (George Bernard Shaw).

Each morning read out loud the following:

I am a peacemaker because...
♡ I show love and understanding.
♡ I avoid criticism.
♡ I return good for evil.
♡ I am considerate and unselfish.
♡ I pray and listen to promptings of the Holy Ghost.

Home is heavenly when I'm a Peacemaker

Peacemaker Pebble:

Give each young woman a pebble with the following note and challenge them to be a peacemaker, helping their entire family to feel peace when they are around.

PEBBLE PROMISE:

This week I will look at this pebble and remember to be a peacemaker. When a pebble is tossed into a pool of water, it creates a ripple, making larger and larger circles, showing how this one pebble's influence is widespread. My one action of being a peacemaker can affect my entire family.

I will be a peacemaker.

Each morning read out loud the following:

I am a peacemaker because...

♡ I show love and understanding.
♡ I avoid criticism.
♡ I return good for evil.
♡ I am considerate and unselfish.
♡ I pray and listen to promptings of
  the Holy Ghost.

Home
is heavenly
when I'm a
Peacemaker.

Lesson 10 — Priesthood: Priesthood Power Is a Blessing
(Priesthood Power Blessings Journal)

PREPARATION: Review chalkboard discussion (p. 39) in *Young Women Manual 2*.

TO MAKE ACTIVITY HANDOUT: *Copy and color the *Priesthood Power Blessings Journal* pages (p. 24-25) for each young woman.

**LESSON MATCH ACTIVITY—*Priesthood Power Blessings Journal:* Have young women write their feelings about how the priesthood has or will bless their lives on these two inspirational journal pages.

COLOR FLORAL SYMBOL:
*Color floral symbol on activity and scripture card. File activity in Young Women "Value-able" Journal behind the value tab.

Divine Nature (blue morning glory)

MIDWEEK ACTIVITIES:

Priesthood Leaders Chalkboard Discussion:
Have a priesthood holder (approved by the bishop) come and give a chalkboard discussion about the priesthood—what it is, what it does, etc.—and tell how young women can assist and support priesthood holders. Talk about respectful ways to act towards the priesthood and priesthood ordinances. Then have young women select a priesthood holder they respect and admire and write them a note of appreciation, telling them what they have observed.

Priesthood Panel Discussion:
Gather a select group of Melchizedek and Aaronic priesthood holders to answer questions about the priesthood. Have the bishop select a panel and prepare participants. Give the bishop a list of questions and have him approve the list and add his ideas.

Honoring the Priesthood Hour:
Have young women prepare an hour-long program to honor the priesthood holders in your ward. Invite all the young men. Have a woman (the bishop's or a counselor's wife) give a tribute to the priesthood holders in the ward. Spotlight several young men and other Melchizedek Priesthood holders, telling why they are admired. Information can be obtained from leaders, bishop, and family members. Have the bishop choose the priesthood holders to spotlight. Serve punch and star-shaped cookies with a note:

Priesthood Holders: You are the stars ☆ ☆ that bring light

Priesthood Power
Blessings Journal

Baby blessing

Baptism

Membership in the Lord's Church

Gift of the Holy Ghost

The sacrament

Priesthood guidance in the home

Write your feelings about how the priesthood has blessed or will bless your life.

Guidance from living prophets and apostles

Priesthood blessing when sick or in need

A father's blessing

Home teachers

A caring bishop

Patriarchal blessing

Temple endowment

Temple marriage

| Lesson 11 | Bishop: Bishop Appreciation |
| | (Thanks a Bunch! Sunflowers in a Pot) |

PREPARATION: Review writing activity (p. 42) in *Young Women Manual 2*.

TO MAKE ACTIVITY: *Copy, color, and cut out the *Thanks a Bunch!* label and glue it to a terra cotta pot. Fill pot with candy or Styrofoam. Have young women write their personal note inside the flower (see *Note Ideas* below). Cut a slit at the top center of the flower to insert flower center tab (smile circle). Tape a straw on the back of the flower. Tape leaf stem to the straw, below the flower. Ask the bishop's wife about his favorite candy, if placing candy in the pot.

LESSON MATCH ACTIVITY—*Thanks a Bunch! Sunflowers in a Pot:* Have young women help you create a *Thanks a Bunch!* flower pot to give to your bishop, filled with sunflower thank-you notes. When young women present pot to bishop, have them read their note and place their flower in the pot. *Note:* Young women may want to do this for their family.

Note Ideas: Thanks for: helping us choose the right, receiving revelation for the ward, shaking hands, helping members repent, being a good example, greetings with a smile, encouraging us to pay tithing and fast offerings, helping us be missionaries, helping needy families, giving interviews for the temple, having a testimony, being a friend, calling good leaders, visiting ward members, helping with funerals, supervising leaders, praying and fasting for ward members, counseling and helping with problems, teaching the gospel.

COLOR FLORAL SYMBOL:

*Color floral symbol on activity and scripture card. File activity in Young Women "Value-able" Journal behind the value tab.

| *Good Works (yellow sunflower)* |

MIDWEEK ACTIVITIES:

Cook the Bishop His Favorite Dessert:
Ask the bishop's wife what his favorite dessert is. Make, decorate, and deliver. For example, bake a pie and decorate the top, using frosting in a tube to create a man's shirt collar and tie. Present to the bishop.

Bishop Honor Night:
Have the bishop's wife help plan and prepare the activity. Spotlight him, telling about his hobbies or things he likes to do and things she likes about him. Tell his favorite food and serve some. Involve his family.

Lesson 12 | Blessings: Blessings from Heavenly Father
(Special Blessing Journal)

PREPARATION: Review lesson application (p. 45) in *Young Women Manual 2*.

TO MAKE ACTIVITY HANDOUT: *Copy and color a *Special Blessing Journal* (p. 30) for each young woman.

LESSON MATCH ACTIVITY—*Special Blessing Journal:* Suggest to young women that they obtain a priesthood blessing from their father or bishop. This is nice at the beginning of a school year or when extra help is needed. Have young women fill in their *Special Blessing Journal*, recording words spoken and their thoughts of that special blessing from Heavenly Father.

COLOR FLORAL SYMBOL:

*Color floral symbol on activity and scripture card. File activity in Young Women "Value-able" Journal behind the value tab.

| *Individual Worth (red rose)* |

MIDWEEK ACTIVITIES:

Young Woman's Viewpoint:
Tie this activity in with lesson 10 (p. 39 in the *Young Women Manual 2—#1-14*). Ask young women and other women to share their experiences upon receiving a blessing from the

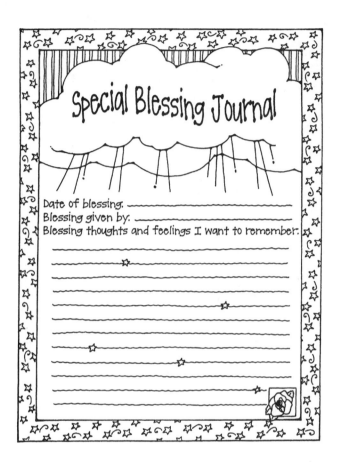

priesthood or special blessing (e.g., blessing from their father, home teacher, or bishop). Talk about the inspiration, faith, and worthiness to receive and give that blessing. Have young women share their feelings on the power they have felt from a blessing and the words of wisdom gathered from that special blessing.

Father or Bishop's View:
Ask several fathers and the bishop, or members of the bishopric, to share their experiences in giving blessings.

Special Blessing Journal

Date of blessing: _____

Blessing given by: _____

Blessing thoughts and feelings I want to remember:

_____

_____

_____

_____

_____

_____

_____

_____

_____

_____

_____

Lesson 13	**Patriarchal Blessing: My Blessing Guides My Life** (Patriarchal Blessing Prep Checklist and Messages Memo)

PREPARATION: Review lesson 13 in *Young Women Manual 2*.

TO MAKE ACTIVITY HANDOUT:
*Copy and color the *Patriarchal Blessing Preparation Checklist* and *Messages Memo* (p. 32-33) for each young woman.

LESSON MATCH ACTIVITY—
Patriarchal Blessing Prep Checklist and Message Memo: Help young women prepare themselves for their patriarchal blessings with this *Blessing Prep Checklist*. Then after receiving their blessing, have them read it with a prayerful heart and record the special messages on the *Patriarchal Blessing Messages Memo*. Encourage them to live worthy to receive the blessings promised.

COLOR SYMBOL:
*Color floral symbol on activity and scripture card. File activity in Young Women "Value-able" Journal behind the value tab.

Individual Worth (red rose)

MIDWEEK ACTIVITIES:

Patriarch Wife's View:
Have the wife of a patriarch come and relate her special insights and experiences regarding patriarchal blessings. She can also tell what she does to support her husband. Tell the steps involved in obtaining a patriarchal blessing, then tell what to do with your patriarchal blessing and how to read and understand it so it will help you throughout your life.

Insights of Living a Patriarchal Blessing:
Have different mothers and older women in the ward who have received their patriarchal blessing share how it has helped them in their life. Discuss how each blessing is different and very personal. If parts of a blessing are shared, approve what is shared with leaders ahead of time.

*All images can be printed in color or black and white using the *Young Women Fun-tastic! Activities—Manual 2* CD-ROM.

Patriarchal Blessing

Preparation Checklist

1. ☐ Be worthy and baptized a member of the Church.

2. ☐ Desire to receive a blessing.

3. ☐ Understand promises in Abraham's blessing (Abraham 2:9-11).

4. ☐ Be mature enough to appreciate the blessing.

5. ☐ Receive a recommend from the bishop.

6. ☐ Make an appointment with the patriarch.

7. ☐ Prepare for the blessing by studying, praying, and fasting.

8. ☐ Pray for patriarch to be inspired.

Patriarchal Blessing

Messages Memo

I was blessed with:

_____
_____
_____
_____
_____

I was promised:

_____
_____
_____
_____
_____

What I must do:

_____
_____
_____
_____
_____

Lesson 14 Temple Blessings: Temple Attendance Brings Great Blessings
(My Value-able List to Earn Temple Blessings)

PREPARATION: Review the entire lesson (p. 50-52) in *Young Women Manual 2.*

TO MAKE ACTIVITY HANDOUT: *Copy and color the *Temple Blessings Poster* (p. 35) for each young woman. Have them color the floral symbols as follows: Faith (white lily), Divine Nature (blue morning glory), Individual Worth (red rose), Knowledge (green ivy), Choice and Accountability (orange poppy), Good Works (yellow sunflower), and Integrity (purple pansy).

LESSON MATCH ACTIVITY—*My "Value-able" List to Earn Temple Blessings*:
1. Read Harold B. Lee's quote on the form (shown right). Tell young women they can have the blessings of the temple as they strive to live the Young Women values.
2. Beside each floral symbol, young women can write what they will do to be temple worthy (using each value as their guide).

COLOR FLORAL SYMBOL:
*Color floral symbol on activity and scripture card. File activity in Young Women "Value-able" Journal behind the value tab.

Integrity (purple pansy)

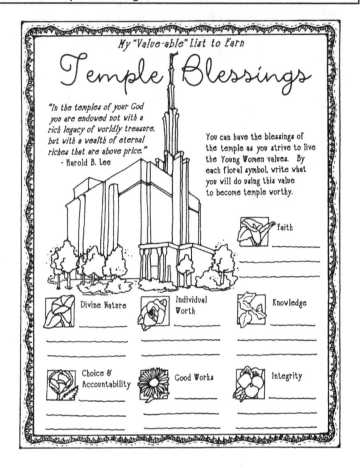

My "Value-able" List to Earn
Temple Blessings

"In the temples of your God you are endowed not with a rich legacy of worldly treasure, but with a wealth of eternal riches that are above price."
- Harold B. Lee

You can have the blessings of the temple as you strive to live the Young Women values. By each floral symbol, write what you will do using this value to become temple worthy.

Faith

Divine Nature   Individual Worth   Knowledge

Choice & Accountability   Good Works   Integrity

MIDWEEK ACTIVITIES:

Temple/Ancient History Tour:
Have an evening of ancient history, and decorate a room with ancient temples drawn on butcher paper. Invite someone to come and talk about ancient temples. Tell why, where, etc., about the very first temples from the time of Adam. Talk about the ordinances and temple ordinances restored by the Prophet Joseph Smith: baptism, confirmation to receive the Holy Ghost, the sacrament, and the temple ordinances of baptism for the dead, marriage, and the sealing of husband and wife so families can be together forever.

Temple Matron Talk:
Invite a temple matron to speak to young women or go with them to the temple where she can speak with them. She can discuss proper dress—including jewelry—to wear in the temple, the basic ordinances performed in the temple, and the sacredness of this holy place. Talk about the reverence that should exist in the temple. Mention the prayer rolls. Young women can call in names to be entered on these prayer rolls. Discuss baptism for the dead and preparing for the temple.

Baptism for the Dead:
Have young women receive a recommend from the bishop and go together to the temple to perform this great work.

Bishop Preview Temple Questions:
The bishop can help young women prepare to enter the temple by asking them to think of the questions he might ask if he were interviewing them for a temple recommend.

My "Value-able" List to Earn
Temple Blessings

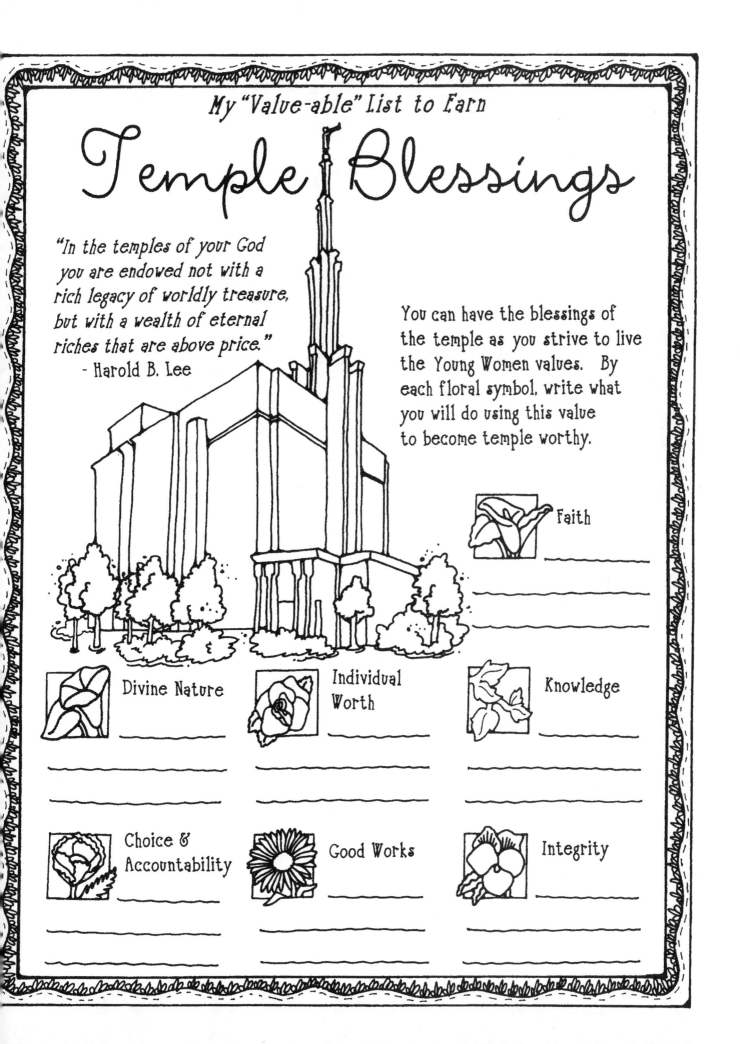

"In the temples of your God you are endowed not with a rich legacy of worldly treasure, but with a wealth of eternal riches that are above price."
- Harold B. Lee

You can have the blessings of the temple as you strive to live the Young Women values. By each floral symbol, write what you will do using this value to become temple worthy.

Faith
_____
_____
_____

Divine Nature
_____
_____

Individual Worth
_____

Knowledge
_____

Choice & Accountability
_____

Good Works
_____

Integrity
_____

Lesson 15 — Temple Marriage: I Will Prepare For Temple Marriage
(Temple Preparation Tent Card)

PREPARATION: Review chalkboard discussion (p. 56) in *Young Women Manual 2*.

TO MAKE ACTIVITY HANDOUT: *Copy, color, and cut out the *Temple Preparation Tent Card* (p. 37) on cardstock for each young woman.

LESSON MATCH ACTIVITY—*Temple Preparation Tent Card:* Help young women create an eternal family by placing the right choices on their own personalized temple tent card. This *Temple Tent Card* stands up so it can be placed on the young woman's dresser or table. Young women can write on one side of the card, things they will do now to prepare for her temple marriage.

Ideas: Be morally clean, respect and support the priesthood, pay tithing, practice the law of the fast, be honest, obey the Word of Wisdom, set a good example, maintain clean speech, pray regularly, honor parents, choose a worthy companion, obey all of God's commandments.

Things I will do now to prepare for my temple marriage:

• Youth should begin today to so order their lives that they will be found worthy at the proper time to go to the House of the Lord and be uplifted and sanctified by the temple ceremony.
—Harold B. Lee

COLOR FLORAL SYMBOL:
*Color floral symbol on activity and scripture card. File activity in Young Women "Value-able" Journal behind the value tab.

Divine Nature (blue morning glory)

MIDWEEK ACTIVITIES:

Temple Marriage Panel:
With the bishop's help, gather together a panel to discuss temple marriage. Choose recently married couples, older couples, and a recently sealed-together family. Have young women write questions ahead of time, asking the bishop to direct a few.

Marriage Museum:
Create a museum of potential marriage companions. Create life-size silhouettes of couples out of colored craft paper and display them on the wall. Divide young women into two teams and give them a marker.

1. Assign one group of young women to write on one silhouette positive traits for an eternal mate that would lead them to an eternal marriage. Assign the second group to write on another silhouette those traits that would lead them away from a temple marriage.

2. Have young women share their lists of ideas.

Things I will do now to prepare for
my temple marriage:

"Youth should begin today to
so order their lives that they
will be found worthy at the
proper time to go to the
House of the Lord and be
uplifted and sanctified by
the temple ceremony."

-Harold B. Lee

| Lesson 16 | Journals: I Will Record My Personal History |
| | (My Journal Lined and Unlined Pages) |

PREPARATION: Review chalkboard discussion (p. 58) in *Young Women Manual 2*.

TO MAKE ACTIVITY HANDOUT: *Copy enough pages to make a journal (p. 39-42) for each young woman.

LESSON MATCH ACTIVITY—*My Journal*: Help young women start a personal history, writing in their journal (using the suggestions on p. 58 in the *Young Women Manual 2*). Provide pages they can add to their current journal entries. Encourage them to place the *My Journal* lined and unlined pages in a looseleaf binder. They can use pages to take notes, add photos, programs, awards, and other special items.

COLOR FLORAL SYMBOL:
*Color floral symbol on activity and scripture card. File activity in Young Women "Value-able" Journal behind the value tab.

| *Good Works (yellow sunflower)* |

MIDWEEK ACTIVITIES:

Cover an Old Journal Binder with Fabric.

"Journal-ism" Journey:
Create the mood for "journal-ism," or journal writing. Set up the room to look like a newsroom filled with back issues of newspapers, articles posted on the wall, typewriter at some tables, and notebooks and pencils on hand. Have several young women come in with hats or badges that read PRESS at the top. Have them come in with pads and pens in hand, anxious to get the story. They ask questions of the young woman leader, who proceeds to give them the details of her life's story. Reporters go around the room asking what others know about this young woman leader and getting interesting facts. Make a large box with an opening and deposit news stories in box. Take time to draw reports out of the box and read them aloud to preview the story.

Time Line Journal Writing:
Have young women sit down at their table with pad and pen and make a time line of five years of their lives by naming five events they wish to write about. Then have them take 10 minutes to write about one or two in detail. Share stories.

Balance Life Journal:
Have a "balanced life night" to help young women try to balance their life each day as Jesus did.
1. Talk about the life of Jesus and how He balanced His life, increasing in wisdom (mental), and stature (physical), and in favor with God (spiritual), and man (social) (see Luke 2:52).
2. Provide a sheet of paper entitled "My Balanced Life Journal" with fives lines each for Mental, Physical, Spiritual, Social areas. Ask young women to think about their day today or yesterday, and write something in each area that tells of their experiences for the day. Tell young women this is one way they can jog their memory each day to record important events. Plus it will help us balance our lives as Jesus did, making the most of each day.
3. Encourage young women to select goals each day in these four areas to help them balance their life.

My Journal

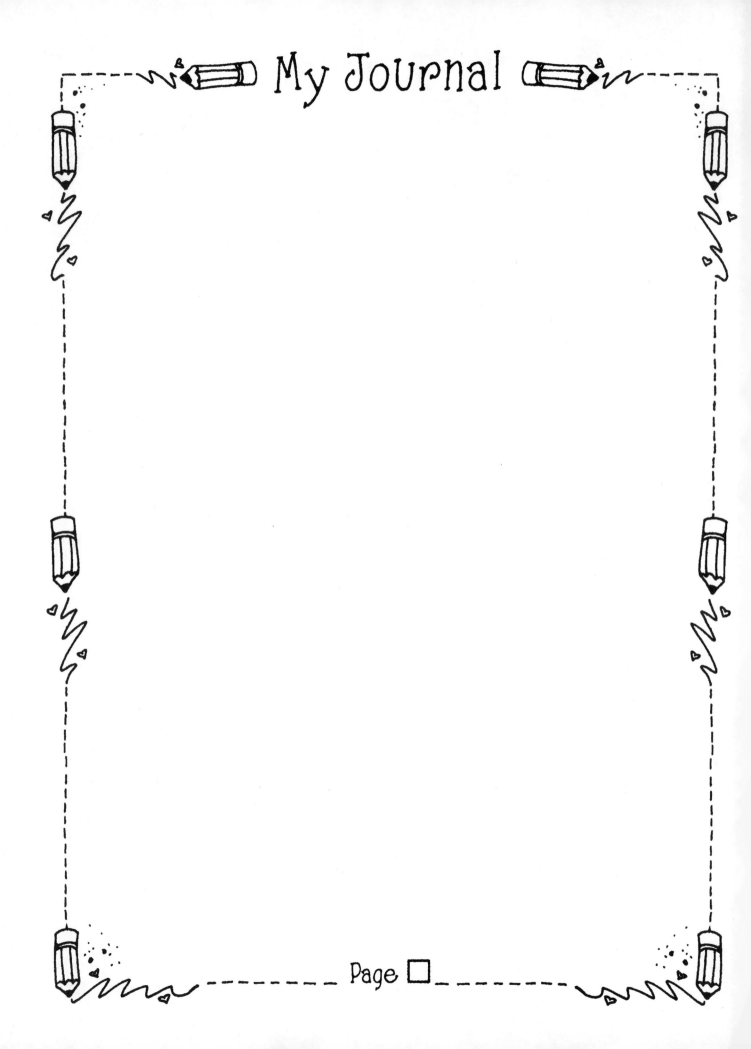

My Journal

My Journal

My Journal

Lesson 17   Family History: I Will Keep Family History Records
(Portrait of My Ancestor)

PREPARATION: Review Class member presentation (page 62) in *Young Women Manual 2.*

TO MAKE ACTIVITY HANDOUT: *Copy and color *Portrait of My Ancestor* (p. 44) for each young woman.

LESSON MATCH ACTIVITY—*Portrait of My Ancestor:* Encourage young women to go through their pedigree chart, learn about and write about their ancestors. Use the *Portrait of My Ancestor* form to write detailed information. Then share this with the other young women in class the following week by having young women spotlight an ancestor using their portrait form as a guide, and encouraging them to photocopy a picture of their ancestor and reduce it to fit the page, or draw a picture/portrait of what they thought that their ancestor looked like.

COLOR FLORAL SYMBOL:
*Color floral symbol on activity and scripture card. File activity in Young Women "Value-able" Journal behind the value tab.

Individual Worth (red rose)

MIDWEEK ACTIVITIES:

Family History Library Name Search:
Visit the Family History library and search a name. Have each young woman get some information from her parents. If no information is found, have someone in the library take them through the research steps. Ask your ward family history representative for help.

Faith-Promoting Family History Experiences:
Ask someone who has been researching their family history to tell of their faith-promoting experiences as they've done family research, submitted names for temple work, and written their family history.

Portrait of
My Ancestor
By: _____

Name: _____
Born: _____
Place: _____
Married: _____
Spouse: _____
Died: _____
Place: _____

How related? _____
_____
_____

Summary of ancestor's history: _____
_____
_____
_____
_____
_____
_____
_____

Baptisms for the Dead:
Inquire if someone in your ward needs work done for some ancestors. While at the temple, ask young women to pay attention to the dates and names that impressed them. Share your experiences afterward around banana splits or ice cream sodas. Ask them how they think those deceased persons, for whom they were baptized, felt that day. Estimate the number of years they may have waited for this great day.

Family Reunion Brainstorm:
Have young women come with their ideas for food, fun, and games for a family reunion. Challenge young women to help their parents plan and organize a family reunion.
Ideas: Hide family photos; the first to find Grandpa Ross wins! Make cupcakes and hide Grandma Ross's name in one. Write her name on a small piece of paper and wrap it in tin foil. Bake it or slip it inside an already-baked cupcake.

Portrait of My Ancestor

By: _____

Name: _____

Born: _____

Place: _____

Married: _____

Spouse: _____

Died: _____

Place: _____

How related? _____

_____

_____

Summary of ancestor's history: _____

_____

_____

_____

_____

_____

_____

_____

_____

Lesson 18 | Traditions: I Will Create Righteous Traditions
(My Righteous Traditions Time Capsule)

PREPARATION: Review chalkboard discussion (p. 65) in *Young Women Manual 2.*

LESSON MATCH ACTIVITY—*Righteous Traditions Time Capsule*: Create a time capsule to record righteous traditions. Review the list of traditions in *Young Women Manual 2* (p. 65).

TO MAKE TIME CAPSULE: *Copy, color, and cut out the *Time Capsule* label and *Righteous Traditions* planner (p. 46) for each young woman.

1. Have them write righteous traditions on the planner. See ideas below. Have young women place the list in the time capsule and sit it in their room, writing the date on the capsule and on their calendar when they will open it.

2. Close the capsule.

Option 1: Have them open it five years from the date sealed.

Option 2: Have them open it every year just to see how they are doing.

Righteous Tradition Ideas: Attend Church as a family each week, obtain a father's blessing before beginning a new school year, visit the sick and elderly often, do dishes together each night, act out the nativity on Christmas Eve, have flag-raising ceremony on patriotic holidays, help the needy, write family and personal history together, do missionary projects together, focus on and try to live a different scripture together each month, prepare special Sunday meals on Saturday, plant and harvest a garden together, plan a family reunion together, ride bikes to the park together for a picnic and scripture reading. Have daily family prayer and weekly family home evening, fast together with a special need in mind each fast Sunday, study the scriptures, Church magazines, and books; etc.

COLOR FLORAL SYMBOL:

*Color floral symbol on activity and scripture card. File activity in Young Women "Value-able" Journal behind the value tab.

Integrity (purple pansy)

MIDWEEK ACTIVITIES:

Sharing of Favorite Family Traditions:
Explain what a tradition is, e.g., a custom or practice. Have each young woman write on a piece of paper one or more of her favorite family traditions. Have each young woman share it with the class. Brainstorm as you make a long list. Have someone take notes and make a list for everyone.
Ideas: Making handmade gifts, making care packages and taking to the sick, placing an upbeat note in a family member's lunch box, getting new pajamas on Christmas Eve, creating a "rainy day box" by collecting small toys and objects for children to play with, playing games every Sunday night.

Revise Old Traditions:
Discuss how traditions have changed; some old ones have changed for the better, some have not. Read a book on etiquette with young women and ask them if they do these thing in their home, e.g., not putting elbows on the table until after they have finished eating, serving family members food from the left instead of the right side, ringing the dinner bell when dinner is ready, putting a heart under the plate of the person who is to give the blessing on the food, lighting a candle when a special guest has come to dinner or when celebrating something well done.

Righteous Traditions

I want to develop...

...now and pass them on to my family.

The righteous habits I want to acquire are:

Time Capsule

My Righteous Traditions

Date sealed

Date to be opened

Time Capsule

My Righteous Traditions

Date sealed

Date to be opened

Lesson 19	Missionary: I Will Prepare to Teach the Gospel
	(Missionary Prep Mirror Motivators)

PREPARATION: Review teacher presentation 1-4 (p. 71-72) in *Young Women Manual 2.*

TO MAKE ACTIVITY HANDOUT: *Copy, color, and cut out the *Missionary Prep Mirror Motivators* (p. 48) for each young woman.

LESSON MATCH ACTIVITY—*Missionary Prep Mirror Motivators*: Give young women a set of these motivators to post on their mirror and write how they can prepare to be a missionary. Share these goals with the young women as a group.

COLOR FLORAL SYMBOL:
*Color floral symbol on activity and scripture card. File activity in Young Women "Value-able" Journal behind the value tab.

Good Works (yellow sunflower)

MIDWEEK ACTIVITIES:

Missionary for a Day:
Have young women learn what a typical week is like in the life of a missionary. Plan a day or a few hours where they can sample it all. Ask sister missionaries to come and tell them what they do. *Ideas:* Reading the scriptures together, going on splits with the missionaries, visiting member neighbors and asking questions about their friends of other faiths, then encouraging members to fellowship them, cooking healthy meals in a hurry, practicing social skills.

School Daze and Missionary Ways Workshop:
Ask young women to divide into teams to discuss ways they can be a missionary at school. Encourage them to show how they can team up to fellowship and befriend less-active girls. They can put on a skit, write a poem, give ideas, make up situations, role-play, or ask questions and talk about being a missionary.

Mission Prep Party:
Give young women a mock missionary badge as they enter the room. Have experts in each area give demonstrations or teach valuable skills.
Ideas: Learn to iron; do laundry; sew on a button; make up healthy menus; learn to cook and prepare food; lead music; introduce yourself; learn about facial expressions, e.g., eye contact; discuss dress and modesty, grooming, posture, manners, how to make friends, and conversation.

IT'S NO BOLOGNA, YOU MUST BUILD YOUR TESTIMONY!

AS I PREPARE TO SHARE THE GOSPEL, I WILL STRENGTHEN MY TESTIMONY BY:

WHEN YOU KNOW, YOU GLOW!

AS I PREPARE TO SHARE THE GOSPEL, I WILL INCREASE MY KNOWLEDGE BY:

IT'S QUITE A THRILL...

...TO HAVE A SKILL!

AS I PREPARE TO SHARE THE GOSPEL, I WILL DEVELOP THE FOLLOWING SKILL:

Lesson 20	Missionary: I Will Share the Gospel
	(Book of Mormon Testimony and Scripture Underlining)

PREPARATION: Review lesson application 33 (p. 77) in *Young Women Manual 2*.

TO MAKE ACTIVITY HANDOUT: *Copy, color, and cut out the *Come Unto Christ Book of Mormon Testimony* page and *Scriptures* list (p. 50) for each young woman.

LESSON MATCH ACTIVITY—*Book of Mormon Testimony and Scripture Underlining*:

1. Give each young woman a copy of the Book of Mormon with the challenge to read it (if they haven't already).

2. Have them pray for a testimony and write their testimony of the Book of Mormon on the *Come Unto Christ* form. Glue this to the inside front of the Book of Mormon.

3. Have young women glue the scripture list to one of the front pages of the Book of Mormon and underline the selected scriptures in red pencil so investigator can turn right to the scriptures.

4. Give the Book of Mormon to a friend or the missionaries. Young women may also include a photo of themselves.

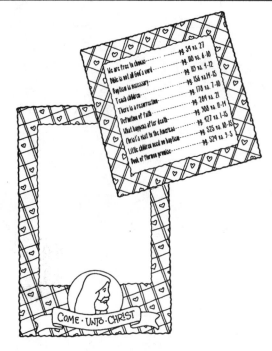

COLOR FLORAL SYMBOL:

*Color floral symbol on activity and scripture card. File activity in Young Women "Value-able" Journal behind the value tab.

Good Works (yellow sunflower)

MIDWEEK ACTIVITIES:

Missionary Discussions to All Young Women:

Have the sister missionaries in your area or a returned sister missionary give the discussions to all young women (over several evenings). Offer the sixth discussion found in the Uniform System for Teaching the Gospel booklets: (1) The Plan of Our Heavenly Father, (2) The Gospel of Jesus Christ, (3) The Restoration, (4) Eternal Progression, (5) Living a Christlike Life, and (6) Membership in the Kingdom.

Share the Gospel Brainstorm:

Have the full-time missionaries come and talk to the young women as a group about those in the area they wish to fellowship. Have the girls prepare questions, ideas, and concerns. Assign young women to fellowship non-LDS or less-active young women.

Friendship Seminar:

Help young women learn how to be a friend and to make friends. This will help them to become better missionaries. Have young women separate into different workshops with different young women or leaders sharing ideas on being a friend. Encourage young women to place questions about being a friend and finding friends in a question box, and then read them aloud. Have the other young women and leaders respond to the questions.

Subjects to Discuss: How to Make a Friend:

· How to keep a friendship going.
· How to know if that person wants to be a friend.
· What if you don't like a person?
· How do you converse with a friend?
· How do you share the gospel with a friend?

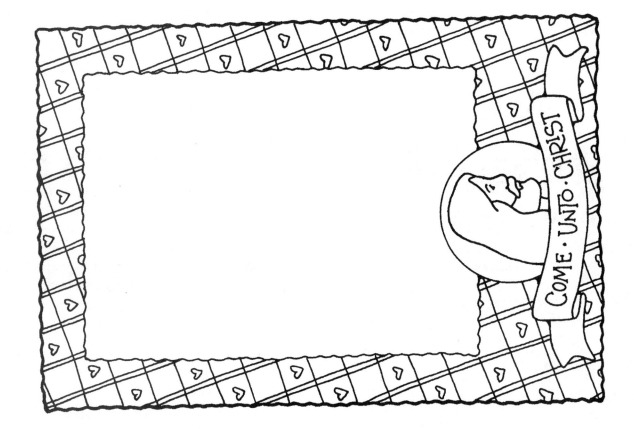

COME · UNTO · CHRIST

Lesson 21 — Missionary: I Will Sustain Missionaries Through Letters

(Missionary Letters Do and Don't List and Postcard)

The Lord will bless his fishers of men!

write about...
- positive feelings
- good experiences
- how pleased you are
- how the Lord is blessing the missionary's family for the work he/she is doing
- your testimony

From:

To:

PREPARATION: Review quotation (p. 79) in *Young Women Manual 2.*

TO MAKE ACTIVITY HANDOUT: *Copy, color, and cut out the post card and Do and Don't List (p. 52) on cardstock for each young woman.

LESSON MATCH ACTIVITY—*Missionary Letters Do and Don't List and Postcard*: Read Proverbs 25:25 to motivate young women to write to missionaries.

Letter Do and Don't List: Give young women a Do and Don't list (p. 52). Review Elder Gordon B. Hinckley's quotation (p. 79 in *Young Women Manual 2*). *Ideas* also found in 1-7 (p. 79-80 in *Manual 2*):

• *Do Write About:* Positive feelings, good experiences, how pleased you are, how the Lord is blessing the missionary's family for the work he/she is doing, your testimony and that of others.

• *Don't Write About:* Problems at home, trivia that doesn't relate to the gospel, romantic thoughts, things you bought or gifts received, dates and parties.

Postcard: Give young women a postcard (p. 52) to write a letter to a missionary; fold it, glue back to back, add postage, and mail.

COLOR FLORAL SYMBOL:
*Color floral symbol on activity and scripture card. File activity in Young Women "Value-able" Journal behind the value tab.

Good Works (yellow sunflower)

MIDWEEK ACTIVITIES:

Panel of Missionary Moms:
Invite mothers of missionaries or returned missionaries to give young women ideas on how to correspond with missionaries. They can answer questions on what to send and to write, plus give tips on sending cookies and other packages. Ask moms how they feel about young women who support their missionary and how they can show their support.

Missionary Letter Writing and Package Sending:
Spend the evening writing letters to missionaries in the ward and preparing care packages. Send cookies in bubble wrap or a box of popcorn. Include motivational, homemade cards in care packages. Young women may wish to create a tape to send with a message from them offering encouragement with missionary work, bearing testimony, reading motivational scriptures, playing and/or singing Church or missionary motivational songs, etc.

Eatable Missionary Cookie Post Cards:
Roll out sugar cookies, cut in squares, and bake ahead for young women to paint. Paint a short testimony message on each cookie card and deliver to the missionaries. Leaders can make cookie cards for young women to take home that reads "The Gospel Is True!" (*Cookie Paint:* Add food coloring to canned milk and paint cookies with paint brushes before or after cookie is baked).

write about...

Do

- positive feelings
- good experiences.
- how pleased you are
- how the Lord is blessing the missionary's family for the work he/she is doing
- your testimony

write about...

Don't

- problems at home
- trivia that doesn't relate to the gospel
- romantic feelings
- things you bought or gifts received
- dates and parties

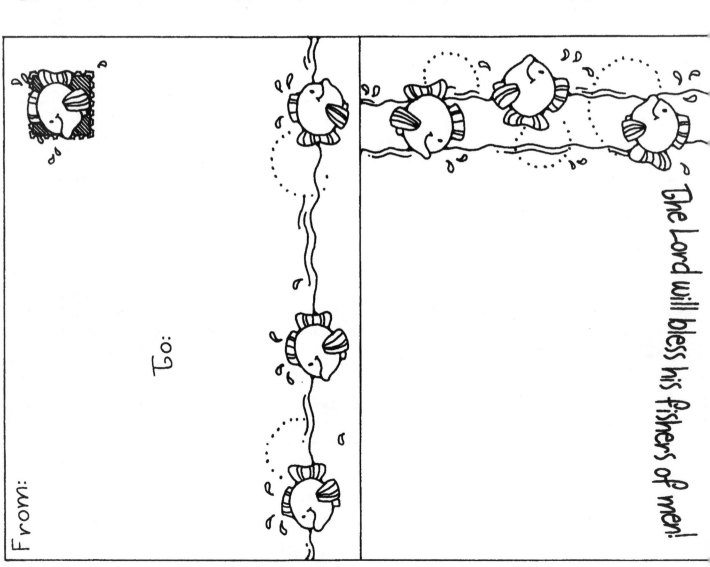

The Lord will bless his fishers of men!

To:

From:

Lesson 22 — Prayer: I Will Counsel with the Lord in Prayer

(Counsel with the Lord Tent Card/Prayer Chart)

PREPARATION: Review lesson application (p. 84 in *Young Women Manual 2*.

TO MAKE ACTIVITY HANDOUT: *Copy, color, and cut out the *Counsel with the Lord Tent Card* (p. 54) on cardstock paper for each young woman. (Cut the young woman's head at the top but not cutting along the top edge.) Fold the top edge of the tent card so card stands up.

LESSON MATCH ACTIVITY—*Counsel with the Lord Tent Card/Prayer Chart:* Help young women make a greater effort to draw close to Heavenly Father through prayer. Read Alma 37:37 and talk about how you can *"counsel with the Lord in all thy doings."* Write how you pray on the card and what to pray for. On the flip side of the card, record for the next thirty days each time you say your morning and night prayers, filling in the box for each day.

COLOR FLORAL SYMBOL:
*Color floral symbol on activity and scripture card. File activity in Young Women "Value-able" Journal behind the value tab.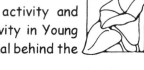

Divine Nature (blue morning glory)

MIDWEEK ACTIVITIES:

Book of Mormon Prayer Presentations:
Ask young women to find and share meaningful scriptures about prayer from the Book of Mormon. Discuss ways they can improve prayers in their daily life from the example of Alma's prayer for his son Alma the Younger (Mosiah 27:14), and Alma the Younger's prayers for the Zoramites with their vain and prideful prayers (Alma 31:12-38).

Make Prayer and Scripture Reminders:
Prayer rocks and angel pillow cases can remind young women to read their scriptures and say their prayers each morning and night. Place rock under pillow with the scriptures nearby.

Pillowcase Craft: Create an angel pillow case embroidered or appliqued with the following: Jesus

said, *"And all things, whatsoever ye shall ask in prayer, believing, ye shall receive"* (Matthew 21:22).

Prayer Rock Craft: Create a prayer rock with the following verse attached:

TO HELP YOU REMEMBER TO SAY YOUR PRAYERS, PLACE THIS ROCK UNDER YOUR PILLOW.
IF YOU GET QUICKLY IN YOUR BED AND FEEL THIS ROCK HIT YOUR HEAD, KNEEL DOWN AND PRAY AND THANK HEAVENLY FATHER FOR YOUR DAY.
ASK HIM FOR HELP IN ALL YOU DO AND KNOW OF HIS GREAT LOVE FOR YOU.

Don't forget to pray!

For the next 30 days, record each time you say your morning and nightly prayers by filling in a box.

	M	N
1		
2		
3		
4		
5		

	M	N
6		
7		
8		
9		
10		

	M	N
11		
12		
13		
14		
15		

	M	N
16		
17		
18		
19		
20		

	M	N
21		
22		
23		
24		
25		

	M	N
26		
27		
28		
29		
30		

"Counsel with the Lord in all thy doings."

Alma 37:37

How to pray:

- _____
- _____
- _____
- _____
- _____
- _____

What to pray for:

- _____
- _____
- _____
- _____
- _____
- _____

Lesson 23	Fasting: Fasting Brings Blessings
	(Try Fasting with Pizza! Doorknob Fasting Reminder)

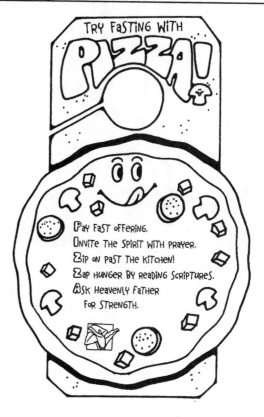

PREPARATION: Review testimony conclusion (p. 88) in *Young Women Manual 2*.

TO MAKE ACTIVITY HANDOUT: *Copy the *PIZZA! Doorknob Fasting Reminder* (p. 56) on cardstock paper for each young woman.

LESSON MATCH ACTIVITY— *Try Fasting with PIZZA! Doorknob Fasting Reminder*: Read Doctrine and Covenants 88:76 and challenge young women to fast and pray each fast Sunday with a purpose. Encourage young women to attach this doorknob reminder to their bedroom door or post on the refrigerator to remind them to fast.

COLOR FLORAL SYMBOL:

*Color floral symbol on activity and scripture card. File activity in Young Women "Value-able" Journal behind the value tab.

Faith (white lily)

MIDWEEK ACTIVITIES:

Fasting Facts:
Gather information and quotes from Church leaders on the proper way to fast, why we fast, and what happens to the body and spirit when we fast. The *Ensign* and *The New Era* are great sources.

Fast Together with a Purpose:
Select a purpose to fast, either individually or as a group. Young women might choose to fast for a less-active young woman they wish to activate, a friend they wish to fellowship, a need in the ward or community, or someone's illness or physical challenge. Make a list of reasons to fast.
Discuss Queen Esther, who fasted to save her people (Esther 4-5).

Scriptures to Share:
- Alma 6:6 (gather to fast and pray)
- D&C 59:13-15 (everyone who can fast should fast)
- Alma 17:3, 9 (helps us feel close to God)
- D&C 88:119, Matthew 6:30-34 (fasting shows faith)
- D&C 88:76 (helps us pray for special blessings)
- Alma 5:46 (fasting and prayer helps us know that things are true by the Spirit of revelation)
- D&C 88:119-120, Mosiah 4:19-21, Matthew 25:35-40, James 1:27, Jacob 2:17-19 (follow fasting by paying fast offerings)
- 3 Nephi 27:1-2, Mosiah 27:22-23 (fast often with others for a cause)
- 2 Corinthians 9:7, D&C 59:15 (fasting should be done cheerfully)
- D&C 59:13 (fasting brings joy)
- Matthew 6:1-4, 16-18 (fast in secret)
- Alma 6:6 (fasting helps in missionary work)

Lesson 24 | # Revelation: I Will Seek Revelation Each Day
(Candle of the Lord Scripture Word Search)

PREPARATION: Review scripture study (p. 90-91) in *Young Women Manual 2*.

TO MAKE ACTIVITY HANDOUT: *Copy and color the *Candle of the Lord Scripture Word Search* (p. 58) for each young woman.

LESSON MATCH ACTIVITY—*Candle of the Lord Scripture Word Search*: Help young women realize that the Lord will light their path as they follow Him. To learn how they can prepare to receive revelation, look up the scriptures and fill in the blanks.

COLOR FLORAL SYMBOL:

*Color floral symbol on activity and scripture card. File activity in Young Women "Value-able" Journal behind the value tab.

Divine Nature (blue morning glory)

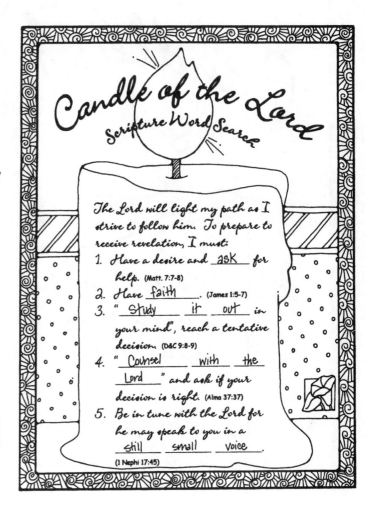

MIDWEEK ACTIVITIES:

Personal Revelation Testimony Time: Have young women take a few moments to look within themselves, then bear their testimonies. Discuss how personal revelation comes when we live the commandments and seek the Spirit through prayer and fasting.

Spiritual Women Spotlight: Spotlight women in the scriptures, e.g.: Abish, Anna, or Queen Ester, who have received revelation (detailed as follows). Talk about these experiences and how we too can rely on the Spirit to guide us.

Abish—Lamanite woman, servant of Lamoni (see Alma 19:16-17, 28-29). Already a convert, she is there when the king, queen, and others in the household fall to the earth; she calls people to king's house, then awakens the queen when the people become fearful.

Anna—prophesied of Jesus' mission, served God in the temple, fasted and prayed day and night (see Luke 2:36-38).

Queen Esther—had great faith, asking the Jews to fast for her (see Esther 4-5).

Candle of the Lord
Scripture Word Search

The Lord will light my path as I strive to follow him. To prepare to receive revelation, I must:

1. Have a desire and _____ for help. (Matt. 7:7-8)

2. Have _____. (James 1:5-7)

3. "_____ ___ _____ in your mind", reach a tentative decision. (D&C 9:8-9)

4. "_____ _____ _____" and ask if your decision is right. (Alma 37:37)

5. Be in tune with the Lord for he may speak to you in a _____ _____ _____.

(1 Nephi 17:45)

Lesson 25   Sacrifice: I Will Understand the Meaning of Sacrifice
(Something to Sacrifice Goal Planner)

PREPARATION: Review discussion (p. 95) and quotation (p. 95-96) in *Young Women Manual 2.*

TO MAKE ACTIVITY HANDOUT: *Copy and color the *Something to Sacrifice Goal Planner* (p. 60) for each young woman.

LESSON MATCH ACTIVITY—*Something to Sacrifice Goal Planner:* Help young women understand the meaning of sacrifice and its importance in their lives using this *Goal Planner.*
1. Read Loren C. Dunn's quote on the planner sheet.
2. Talk about what you might be willing to sacrifice to achieve goals.
3. Have young women use their *Something to Sacrifice Goal Planner* to write three goals they hope to achieve and list one or more sacrifices they must make to achieve success.
4. Read D&C 42:42 and talk about rewards for sacrifice.
5. Ask young women to share at least one way they can share their time, talents, and means to build up the kingdom of God.

COLOR FLORAL SYMBOL:

*Color floral symbol on activity and scripture card. File activity in Young Women "Value-able" Journal behind the value tab.

Good Works (yellow sunflower)

MIDWEEK ACTIVITIES:

Sharing Possessions:
Write down some kind of the service young women are willing to do for one another. You could write several on the board for young women to choose, or you could pull service activities out of a hat.

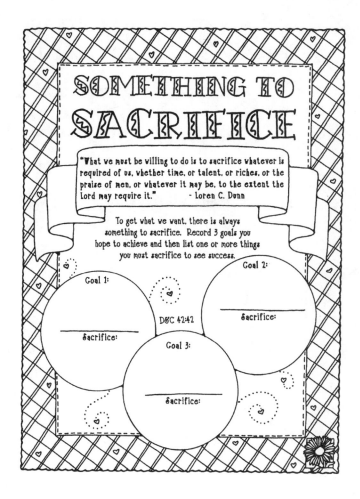

Sharing of Time:
Spotlight several young women who have achieved Personal Progress goals that require sharing of time. Ask them to share how it felt to serve.

Talent Show Time:
Allow each young woman to share one or two talents to give others ideas. You could display something they have created (e.g., craft, painting, music or song composed or performed, story or poem written, a dramatic reading, etc.)

SOMETHING TO SACRIFICE

"What we must be willing to do is to sacrifice whatever is required of us, whether time, or talent, or riches, or the praise of men, or whatever it may be, to the extent the Lord may require it."   - Loren C. Dunn

To get what we want, there is always something to sacrifice. Record 3 goals you hope to achieve and then list one or more things you must sacrifice to see success.

Goal 1:

_____
Sacrifice:

Goal 2:

_____
Sacrifice:

D&C 42:42

Goal 3:

_____
Sacrifice:

Lesson 26	Sacrament: I Will Choose the Right
	(Sacrament Thought Card)

PREPARATION: Review testimony (p. 100) in *Young Women Manual 2.*

TO MAKE ACTIVITY HANDOUT: *Copy, color, and cut out the *Sacrament Thought Card* (p. 62) for each young woman. Fold in half and glue back-to-back.

LESSON MATCH ACTIVITY—*Sacrament Thought Card:* Help young women choose the right by remembering the sacrifice their Savior, Jesus Christ, made for them. They can put this *Sacrament Thought Card* in their scriptures as a reminder. Read Doctrine and Covenants 20:75 and Mosiah 5:7 to learn of actions that help them grow closer to the Savior. Have the young women write their feelings and thoughts of Jesus Christ on the back of the thought card.

COLOR FLORAL SYMBOL: *Color floral symbol on activity and scripture card. File activity in Young Women "Value-able" Journal behind the value tab.

Choice & Accountability (orange poppy)

MIDWEEK ACTIVITY:

Last Supper:
Create a setting like the Last Supper, displaying pita bread (not to be eaten) in the center of the table.
1. As young women sit around the table have them imagine what it would be like to be one of the 12 Apostles, sitting with the Savior, partaking of the sacrament for the first time where Jesus asked them to always remember Him and keep His commandments.
2. Select a conference talk on the sacrament and use unleavened bread (or pita bread) to show what bread was like in the Savior's day.
3. Have them imagine themselves partaking of the sacrament each week and how they feel, being able to partake of such a sacred ordinance.
4. Have them project themselves into the future, always being worthy to partake of the sacrament and renewing their covenants they made at baptism.
5. Review the sacrament prayers found in the Book

of Mormon (3 Nephi 18:7, 11). Have someone who is particularly appreciative of the sacrament express his or her feelings about this sacred ordinance.
6. Have everyone bring their scriptures to have a Sacrament Scripture Chase. Divide into two teams and race to find scriptures on the following, announcing subject matter first, then the scripture.
Scriptures:
▫ Priesthood ordinance (3 Nephi 18:15)
▫ Sacrament given to the Nephites after Christ's resurrection (3 Nephi 18:1-12)
▫ Importance of taking the sacrament each Sunday in sacrament meeting (D&C 20:75)
▫ Reminder of baptismal promises (D&C 20:37 Mosiah 18:6-10)
▫ Helps us think of Jesus and find peace (D&C 19:23-24)
▫ Reminds us that Jesus took our sins upon him (Hebrews 9:28; 13:12, Mosiah 3:5-8)
▫ Jesus is the gate through which we enter heaven (John 14:6, 2 Nephi 9:41)
▫ Jesus suffered and gave his life for us so that we might have a remission of our sins (John 19:16-20, Mosiah 4:1-2, Alma 4:14-15, 2 Nephi 2:6-9)

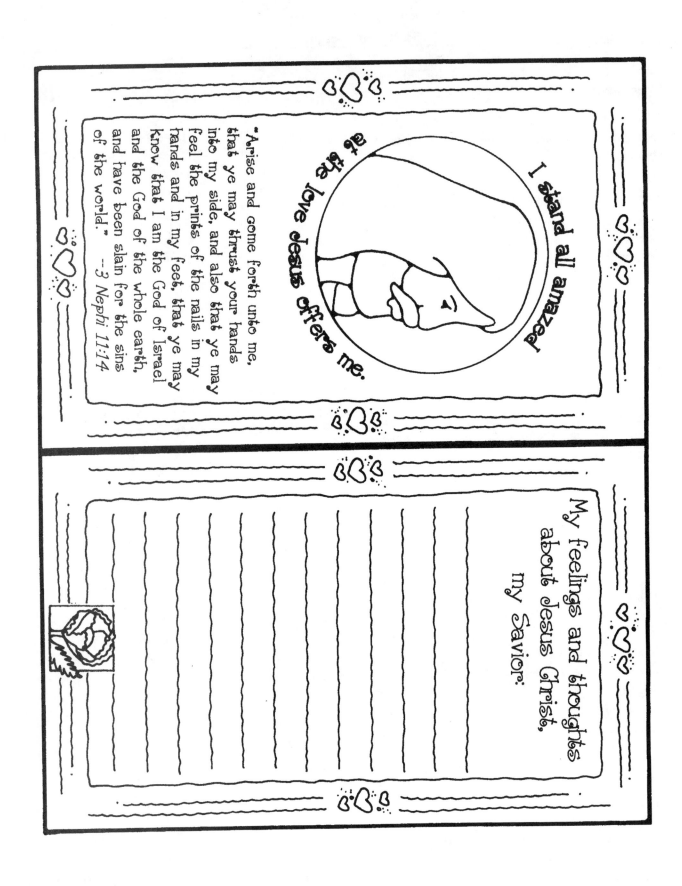

I stand all amazed

at the love Jesus offers me.

"Arise and come forth unto me,
that ye may thrust your hands
into my side, and also that ye may
feel the prints of the nails in my
hands and in my feet, that ye may
know that I am the God of Israel
and the God of the whole earth,
and have been slain for the sins
of the world."
—3 Nephi 11:14

My feelings and thoughts
about Jesus Christ,
my Savior.

Lesson 27 **Testimony: Testimony Is Strengthened Through Obedience**
(Testimony Lost & Found Match Game)

PREPARATION: Review chalkboard discussion "Testimonies Are Weakened Through Disobedience" (p. 103) in *Young Women Manual 2.*

TO MAKE ACTIVITY HANDOUT: *Copy, color, and cut out the *Testimony Lost and Found Match Game* (p. 64-66) (two sets of cards and one label) for each young woman. Slip label inside a plastic zip-close bag and insert the cards.

LESSON MATCH ACTIVITY—*Testimony Lost and Found Match Game*: Create a *Testimony Lost-and-Found Game* to show actions that strengthen and weaken a testimony.

Lesson Ideas Using Cards:

Step 1: Place cards for actions that strengthen testimony in front of young women and say, "We can gain a testimony as we obey the commandments of God. Obedience strengthens our testimony, making us stronger so that we can resist temptation."

Step 2: Place cards for actions that weaken the testimony in front of young women and say, "We can lose a testimony as we disobey the commandments of God. Disobedience weakens our testimony making us weak, making it harder to resist temptation."

To Play Match Game:

1. Divide young women into two teams with a bag full of cards in front of them.

2. Have teams take turns drawing two cards at a time from the bag. If they make a match, they can keep the cards for their team. If no match is made, they lay the cards back facedown on the floor or table.

3. To select their match, the next player can either draw one or two cards from the bag or from those face lying down.

4. When a match is made, have young woman tell how this will strengthen or weaken their testimony.

5. Once all the matches are made, count the cards. The team with the most cards wins!

COLOR FLORAL SYMBOL:

*Color floral symbol on activity and scripture card. File activity in Young Women "Value-able" Journal behind the value tab.

Faith (white lily)

MIDWEEK ACTIVITY:

Testimony Trail Cowgirl and/or Cowboy Party:
(*Fun Option:* Invite young men to participate.)
1.) Select several young women and leaders to create the trail by first drawing a map on paper to know where to place clues and how to get through the maze. 2.) To set up trail, place the tape on the floor leading different directions. 3.) Tape clues that help you decide which direction to go at all turning points, e.g., "Turn left at Howdy Lane if you played poker." "Turn right at Howdy Lane if you walked a little old lady across the street." 4.) Divide young women into two groups, or if young men are invited, girls can compete with boys. 5.) Teams take turns. At "go," time them to see who gets through the maze in the shortest amount of time. 6.) For the next team, reset the clues at the turning points (marked on your map, see #1). Clues could be laced in straws, balloons, placed in envelopes, under a rock, inside a box, under a bucket, etc. 7.) The team that makes it to Happy Valley first wins!

Was asked on a date before I turned 16 but I politely declined.

Participated in a service project.

Was disrespectful to my teacher when he tried to help me.

Was kind to my friend even though she was spreading rumors about me.

Thought about the Savior during the sacrament.

Skipped Sunday School and went for a walk instead.

Drank alcohol just to see what it tasted like.

Prayed when I didn't feel like praying.

Avoided looking at suggestive sites on the Internet.

Wore immodest clothes because all the popular girls wore them.

Volunteered to baby-sit so Mom and Dad could go to the temple.

Watched an R-rated movie because it won an Oscar.

Lied to my parents to avoid punishment.

Smoked a cigarette just to be sociable.

Paid my tithing even though it was difficult.

Read my scriptures every day regardless of how tired I sometimes felt.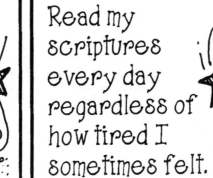

Went to a party where alcohol was being served.

Invited my new friend to a church activity.

Listened to music that lifted my spirit.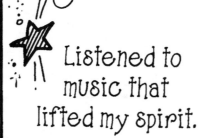

Came home on time even though the party had just started.

Lesson 28	Agency: I Have the Freedom to Choose
	(Consequences Quiz)

PREPARATION: Review discussion (p. 106) in *Young Women Manual 2.*

TO MAKE ACTIVITY HANDOUT: *Copy and color the *Consequences Quiz* (p. 68) for young woman.

LESSON MATCH ACTIVITY—*Consequences Quiz:* Help young women realize that there is a consequence for every action. Have young women complete the quiz. Next to each choice they can write the immediate consequence, the future consequence, and the eternal consequence of that choice or action.

Panel Poll: After completing the activity, divide young women into three groups, each representing a panel that comments on each decision. Panel 1 could have a strip of paper in front of them that reads "Immediate Consequences," Panel 2 a "Future Life" sign, and Panel 3 an "Eternal Consequences" sign. Read each choice and have the panel express their opinion about the choice.

Discuss Making Choices Ahead: Read Genesis 39 and tell about Joseph who was sold into Egypt. When he resisted the advances of Potiphar's wife, he ran (verse 12) from her because he had made up his mind ahead of time what to do. We can do the same by writing choices for the future in our journal. Discuss the possible immediate, future, and eternal consequence if he hadn't resisted temptation.

COLOR FLORAL SYMBOL:

*Color floral symbol on activity and scripture card. File activity in Young Women "Value-able" Journal behind the value tab.

Choice & Accountability (orange poppy)

MIDWEEK ACTIVITY:

Debtors Prison or Partners Paradise:

Ahead of time decorate the room with prison bars. Place a sign for "Debtors Prison" on one side and one for "Partners Paradise" on the other (add beautiful flowers and a pretty backdrop). Write good and bad choices on cards and tape cards on the walls facedown. Prepare at least one or two cards for each young woman.

Consequence Quiz handout illustration

1. Have young women stand in the center of the room as you explain that we owe Heavenly Father a great deal for the blessings we have. We can never really pay back our debts to Him, but we can show our gratitude through our actions. We can live the commandments and make right choices (which will benefit us as well). If we don't make right choices, we get deeper in debt. If we make right choices we grow more like Heavenly Father and become a "partner in paradise." Point to the Partners Paradise corner. Paradise is a place where we are happy and feel loved.

2. Have young women take a card off the wall and take turns reading cards aloud to determine where they go, to Debtors Prison or Partners Paradise. Do this until everyone has had a turn and has gone to their destination.

3. Ask them how their own debts make them feel.

4. Ask them, "With the decision you read, how do you feel about where you are?" Give them a chance to respond. Ask, "Do you feel trapped?" "Do you feel free?"

5. Talk about repentance and service, bearing testimony, etc., as ways to pay back our debts.

Consequence Quiz

Every choice has a consequence! Next to each choice, write down what the immediate, future and eternal consequences would be. Remember to always <u>think</u> before you choose.

Choice:	Immediate Consequences:	Future Consequences:	Eternal Consequences:
Bear my testimony			
Date members of other faiths			
Say prayers daily			
Associate with people of questionable moral character			
Smoke a cigarette			
Attend YW activities only when I feel like it			
Dress immodestly			
Tell the truth			

Lesson 29	Exaltation: I Will Earn the Gift of Eternal Life
	(Premortal, Earth Life, and Exaltation Mobile)

PREPARATION: Review quotations and discussions (p. 109-110) in *Young Women Manual 2.*

TO MAKE ACTIVITY HANDOUT: *Copy, color, and cut out the *Premortal, Earth Life, and Exaltation Mobile* (p. 70-72) on cardstock for each young woman. Have young women write their promised blessings in the blanks (ideas shown below). Fold circles in the center. Place a 15-inch string in the center and glue back to back, leaving a string at the top to hang like a mobile. See ideas below.

LESSON MATCH ACTIVITY—*Premortal, Earth Life, and Exaltation Mobile*: Help young women create this mobile to remind them how they can be worthy of exaltation. *Mobile Ideas:*

Things I Promised in Premortal Life to Do on Earth:
☆ Keep my life clean.
☆ Marry in the temple.
☆ Raise a family and teach them righteousness.

Things I Must Do on Earth to Gain Exaltation:
☆ Have faith in Jesus Christ, repent, be baptized, and receive the Holy Ghost.
☆ Observe the law of strict virtue and chastity.
☆ Be charitable, benevolent, tolerant, and pure.
☆ Devote both talent and material means to spread truth and uplift the race.
☆ Receive temple endowment.
☆ Keep the commandments and endure to the end.

Blessings I Will Receive If I Am Worthy of Exaltation in the Celestial Kingdom:
☆ Godhood, having all things subject to me.
☆ Having angels subject to me.
☆ Having all power and dominion.
☆ Becoming creators of other spirits and other worlds.
☆ Living with Jesus.

COLOR FLORAL SYMBOL:
*Color floral symbol on activity and scripture card. File activity in Young Women "Value-able" Journal behind the value tab.

Divine Nature (blue morning glory)

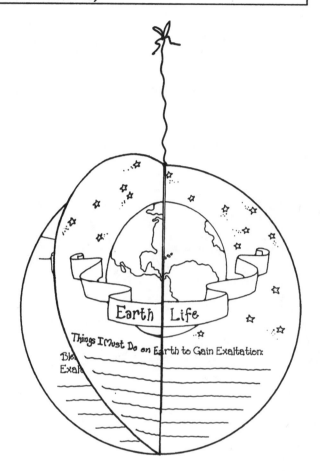

MIDWEEK ACTIVITY:

Jewels in My Crown Service Project:
1. Have young women decide ahead of time what to do for a service project or projects.
2. Have young women put their names on slips of paper and draw from the container to divide into groups of four or more to complete each service project. Make sure those who come late end up in a group.
3. Use the Lesson 3 activity Jewels in My Crown Service List (page 7). Gather after service project and have young women list the goal on their Service List and share their experiences.
4. Serve crown cupcakes. Frost, then use tube frosting to draw a yellow crown on cookie. Place four or five jelly bean jewels on top.

Premortal Life

Things I Promised in My Premortal Life to Do on Earth: _____

_____

_____

_____

_____

Fold

Earth Life

Things I Must Do on Earth to Gain Exaltation:

Fold

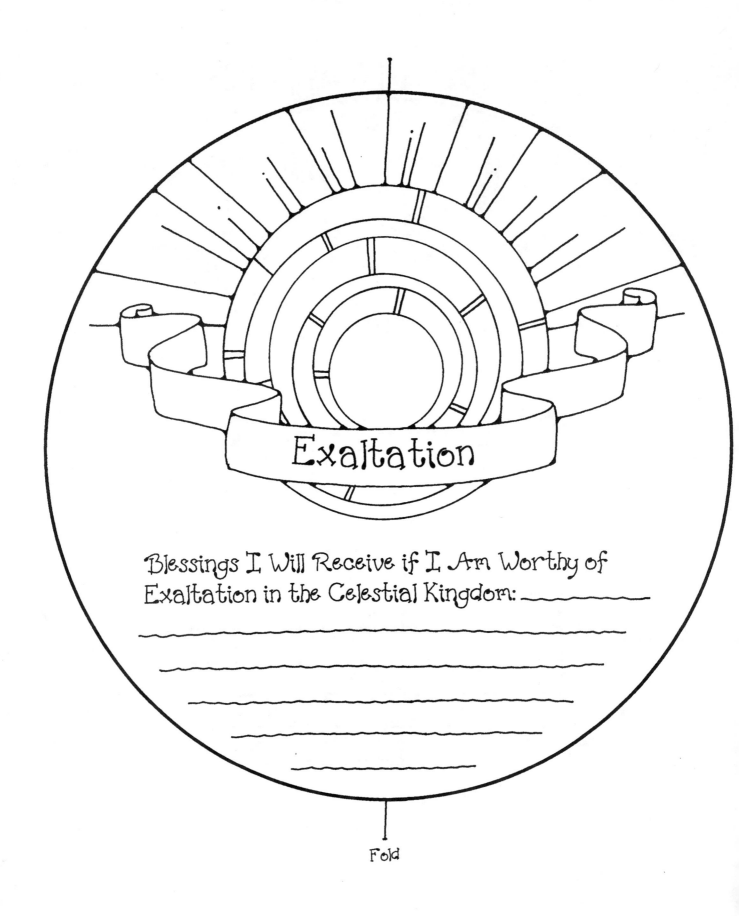

Exaltation

Blessings I Will Receive if I Am Worthy of
Exaltation in the Celestial Kingdom: _____

_____

_____

_____

_____

Fold

Lesson 30 — Testimony: My Testimony Is Strengthened Through Service
(My Gifts of Service Planner)

PREPARATION: Review writing activity (p. 113) in *Young Woman Manual 2*.

TO MAKE ACTIVITY HANDOUT: *Copy and color the *Gifts of Service Planner* (p. 74) for each young woman.

LESSON MATCH ACTIVITY—*My Gifts of Service Planner:* Have young women use this planner to write down ways they can give the gift of service to their family, friends, and to the Church. Review the following examples:

❤ We will SERVE OUR FAMILY by helping, giving of our time, and teaching others.

❤ We will SERVE OUR FRIENDS by sharing, caring, and listening.

❤ We will SERVE AT CHURCH by listening, participating, and showing reverence.

COLOR FLORAL SYMBOL:

*Color floral symbol on activity and scripture card. File activity in Young Women "Value-able" Journal behind the value tab.

Faith (white lily)

MIDWEEK ACTIVITIES:

Service in a Bottle:

Make a list of service ideas on slips of paper and place them in a bottle with the lid on. Place heart stickers on bottle. Tell young women that others don't know we love them unless we show them through our service. If we have a desire to serve others, we need to "do it." If we keep our ideas of service bottled up in our head and never take off the lid, we will never feel the joy that can come from service. Ask young women to find ways to serve throughout the week, then give them the opportunity to share their experiences the following week. Ask them to think about their testimony of the Savior as they serve and share how that service has strengthened their testimony or feelings of self-worth.

Service Detectives:

1. Assign four young women ahead of time to bring dark glasses and lead the others in this fun secret service mission.

2. Divide young women into four groups led by the four young women wearing dark glasses. Tell them they are on a mission to write codes (mystery-service words) for service detectives to find. Follow group instructions below. Give the groups time to write their code.

3. Young women now gather together to guess the mystery service clues not in their group. Give them five minutes, each with a paper and pencil. Each girl writes down the mystery service word(s) from each group.

4. Award prizes for those who guessed the mystery words. (Prize: Smarties or Lifesaver candies.)

Group 1 Symbol Codes: Think up a mystery service and write it in symbols instead of letters. Then write the letters A-Z with the symbols that represent the letters below, e.g., an apple is the letter "a."

Group 2 Hidden Messages: Think up a mystery service and write the words backwards. Use one card for each word and tape cards to the wall randomly.

Group 3 Rebus Writing: Think up a mystery service and write using words, letters, and pictures, e.g., the word "that" would read "T + [a hat picture]."

Group 4 Picture Clues: Think up a service and draw pictures on cards using a different card for each word.

My Gifts of Service

Write down ways you can give the gift of service to family, friends and to the Church. Pick one from each category and wrap up this week in the joy of service!

Family:
♡ _____
♡ _____
♡ _____
♡ _____
♡ _____

Friends:
♡ _____
♡ _____
♡ _____
♡ _____
♡ _____

Church:
♡ _____
♡ _____
♡ _____
♡ _____
♡ _____

A person wrapped up in herself is a very small package.

Lesson 31	Patriotism: I Love My Country!
	(I Love My Country! Community Service Find)

PREPARATION: Review handout (p. 118) in *Young Women Manual 2*.

LESSON MATCH ACTIVITY—*I Love My Country! Community Service Find:* Encourage young women to show their love for their country by contributing to their community. To complete the form, fill in the blanks to show how you can get involved. If they have other ideas, record them on the back.

TO MAKE ACTIVITY HANDOUT: *Copy the *Community Service Find* (p. 76) for each young woman.

COLOR FLORAL SYMBOL:
*Color floral symbol on activity and scripture card. File activity in Young Women "Value-able" Journal behind the value tab.

Good Works (yellow sunflower)

MIDWEEK ACTIVITIES:

Museum Imagination:
Take young women to a museum in your community and have them choose an item that sparks their imagination (e.g., clothing, furniture, china, weapons, wagons, jewelry, shoes, books, etc.). Have them write down the feelings they had when they saw the item. Take a second tour later and share together the possible history of the item. Also see p. 105 in the *Young Women Manual 2* (Midweek Activity 3 for Lesson 45).

Government Official Letter:
Take the time to write a letter to your mayor, commissioner, senator, or president thanking them for something positive they have done. Visit the library or contact their office ahead of time to find the address and issues relating to your city, county, state, and country. Draft a letter together that young women can sign. Check the newspapers beforehand to find issues to relay to the young women (efforts to stop abortion, pornography, drugs, etc.)

School, Church, or Community Cleanup:
Have young women bring their cleaning supplies,

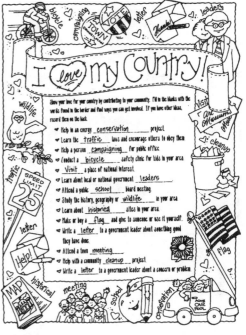

gardening tools, etc., and spend an hour our two cleaning up the community. Take a photo of the young women at work or afterwards to show their parents they have community pride. This same action can be done for an elderly person or couple.

Children's Patriotic Parade:
Have young women work with the Primary and neighborhood children to put on a patriotic parade during your country's annual celebration. Children can parade down the local neighborhood streets showing off their decorated wagons or bikes and wearing their native costume or patriotic colors. They can decorate their transportation with ribbon or crepe paper in the colors of your nation's flag. Purchase small flags to wave. Send out notices to neighbors ahead, telling them the date, time, and parade route (providing a map showing the beginning and ending destination). Provide patriotic music to march by. For the final activities, give children a pony ride and a popsicle or ice-cream treat.

Law Discussion:
Read Alma 42 and discuss why we have laws and how living them brings freedom.

Constitutional Tour and/or Books:
Tour your local capitol or other government building and discuss the Constitution or laws of the land and/or read a patriotic book together on several evenings; do so with hot cocoa and treats. Read historic documents of your country, e.g., for Americans, read the Gettysburg Address, or Patrick Henry's speech "Give Me Liberty, or Give Me Death," given to the Virginia Convention in 1775 (see *History of the United States* by George Bancroft, 1858).

I ❤️ love my Country!

Show your love for your country by contributing to your community. Fill in the blanks with the words found in the border and find ways you can get involved. If you have other ideas, record them on the back.

- ♥ Help in an energy _____ project.
- ♥ Learn the _____ laws and encourage others to obey them.
- ♥ Help a person _____ for public office.
- ♥ Conduct a _____ safety clinic for kids in your area.
- ♥ _____ a place of national interest.
- ♥ Learn about local or national government _____.
- ♥ Attend a public _____ board meeting.
- ♥ Study the history, geography or _____ in your area.
- ♥ Learn about _____ sites in your area.
- ♥ Make or buy a _____ and give to someone or use it yourself.
- ♥ Write a _____ to a government leader about something good they have done.
- ♥ Attend a town _____.
- ♥ Help with a community _____ project.
- ♥ Write a _____ to a government leader about a concern or problem.

bicycle

campaigning

TOWN councilman

VOTE

letter

Thanks!

...leaders

Wildlife

Visit

art Museum

Music

cleanup

traffic

SPEED LIMIT 25

letter

Help!

flag

MAP

historical

meeting

School

conservation

ACME CAR POOL

Lesson 32	Life: Life Is Sacred
	(Life Is Sacred! Lullaby Lollipop)

PREPARATION: Review quote from Melvin J. Ballard (p. 123) in *Young Women Manual 2.*

TO MAKE ACTIVITY HANDOUT: *Copy, color, and cut out the *Lullaby Lollipop* covers (p. 78) for each young woman. Glue circles back-to-back on left and right, leaving top and bottom open to slide lollipop inside. Tie a pretty ribbon at the bottom ("tie a knot," indicating an honorable marriage). *Option:* Tie two lifesavers in ribbon/knot to represent wedding rings.

LESSON MATCH ACTIVITY—*Life Is Sacred! Lullaby Lollipop*: Help young women realize the importance of marriage and family.

COLOR FLORAL SYMBOL:
*Color floral symbol on activity and scripture card. File activity in Young Women "Value-able" Journal behind the value tab.

Choice & Accountability (orange poppy)

MIDWEEK ACTIVITIES:

Babysitting Basket:
Have young women come with a basket full of items that they might take babysitting and take turns showing these items. Give each young woman paper and a pencil to make note of items they might include in their basket.

Baby First-Aid:
Have a nurse or CPR expert tell how to care for a baby who stops breathing, or how to deal with burns, cuts, or other injuries. Practice CPR on both large and small dolls. Have young women and mothers share experiences they have had rescuing or caring for a child. From a first-aid handbook, copy pages teaching first-aid techniques. Assign these to several young women, who can report later on what they've learned.

Bathing Babies Demo:
Have a nurse from the hospital show young women how to bathe a baby or arrange for young women to visit a training class for new mothers.

Life is sacred!

Swim Rescue and Swim Games:
Take young women swimming and have a trained lifeguard show them how to rescue a child from drowning. You can also show young women games that children can play in a pool.

Children's Baby Party:
Have young women plan and present a baby party for small children, ages 4-6. Have young women bring a child and two baby bottles. Fill the bottles with punch or colored water to drink during the party. Have young women bring a picture of themselves as a child and also one of their small guest. Use pictures for Guess Who? game. Young women should also be prepared to share their favorite game or activity with the children. Watch a movie that relates to babies. Play Ring-around-the Rosies, London Bridges, Hide-and-Go-Seek, and Laundry Basket Basketball.

Relief Society Nursery Service:
Have young women serve in the nursery for an enrichment meeting. Preplan activities, stories, and, treats.

New Mother Reflections:
Have a new mother talk about her experiences as a mother, compared to what she expected before she was married.

Life is sacred!

"The greatest mission of women is to give life, earth life, through honorable marriage, to waiting spirits, our Father's spirit children who anxiously desire to come to dwell here in this mortal state."

~Melvin J. Ballard

Life is sacred!

"The greatest mission of women is to give life, earth life, through honorable marriage, to waiting spirits, our Father's spirit children who anxiously desire to come to dwell here in this mortal state."

~Melvin J. Ballard

Lesson 33	**Chastity: I Will Honor the Sacred Power of Procreation**
	(Caution! It's a Jungle Out There! Quicksand Blackout Puzzle)

PREPARATION: Review Resource Material (p. 130) in *Young Women Manual 2*.

TO MAKE ACTIVITY HANDOUT: *Copy and color *Quicksand Puzzle* (p. 81) for each young woman.

LESSON MATCH ACTIVITY—

***CAUTION!* It's a Jungle Out There!** *Quicksand Blackout Puzzle*:

1. Tell young women that the quicksand in the jungle of life is not easily seen. Satan camouflages evil, making it appear good and right. He sets traps and pits, like quicksand, all around us. If we get too close we can fall into them. Sometimes youth want to try something for themselves to see what it feels like, or they feel they can handle a situation and just go in part way. But even putting a toe into the deadly sand, letting down their guard, can pull them in deeper until they are trapped in his powerful quicksand trap.

2. Have young women color and complete the puzzle to avoid Satan's traps and stay on the right trail.

Answers (starting top to bottom):

Quicksand Traps: masturbation, necking, dirty jokes, staying out late, petting, pornography, impure thoughts, immodesty, fornication, homosexuality, R rated movies.

Chastity Trail: group activities, listen to counsel, uplifting music, virtuous thoughts, prayer, true friendship, scripture reading, courage to say no, clean speech, obey parents.

In the puzzle you must find and circle 10 things that will keep you out of the quicksand (Satan's traps) and on the right trail (chastity) in your journey through the jungle (world). If you stumble into the quicksand cross out the word before you start to sink! The word or word groups are read from left to right or backwards, right to left.

3. See quicksand Midweek Activity 1 (shown right).

COLOR FLORAL SYMBOL:

*Color floral symbol on activity and scripture card. File activity in Young Women "Value-able" Journal behind the value tab.

Choice & Accountability (orange poppy)

See *Midweek Activities* on the following page . . .

MIDWEEK ACTIVITIES:

It's a Jungle Out There! Quicksand Traps:

1. Set up a jungle scene with brown wrapping paper in the center to represent quicksand. Place a nice lounge chair with an umbrella and an intriguing drink on top of the quicksand.

2. Take young women through the jungle scene and end up focusing on the lounge chair scene. Tell young women that below the chair is quicksand. They would naturally stay away from quicksand if they knew it was there. But Satan's traps are often disguised by trees in the jungle or in our lives by attractive objects or words that entice. Talk about Satan's quicksand traps to pull you under into necking, petting, intimacy, and sex. If we put our toe in the quicksand, we are tempted to go further until our feet and legs are stuck, and soon we are sitting in the quicksand. Before we realize it, we are up to our necks in Satan's trap.

3. Have young women sit down and write questions on slips of paper and place them in a box. Have leaders and young women talk about questions and how to avoid quicksand traps. Plan what to say in situations where it may be difficult to say no (e.g., at a party if alcohol is offered and we drink, we can then easily lose control). Heavenly Father knows our thoughts but Satan does not have that power. Satan can only read our actions. If we give in a little, he tempts us further. Don't give him control by letting go of your values.

Chastity Talk and Chastity Choices:

1. *Speaker:* Have a guest speaker talk about chastity choices. Bishops are very good at talking on this subject; so are their wives. Seminary teachers are also good resources.

2. *Discussion:* After a guest speaker, help young women project themselves into the future to look at choices they will make. Compare dating a boy who is good (chaste) to dating a boy who is unchaste. Talk about group dates as opposed to single dating. Talk about the daily spiritual nourishment needed to help you make chaste choices.

Eternal Companion "Chew"sing Choices:

Give each person a piece of chewing gum to chew.

Activity 1: As they chew have them close their eyes and think of the "chew"sing they will do to find their eternal companion. Each choice they "chews" will either guide them to their eternal companion or farther away.

Activity 2: After chewing they can pass the chewed piece to the next person. Ask, "Do you want to have a piece of gum that is already chewed?" Think of being an unchewed piece of gum (being chaste and pure) as opposed to being a chewed piece (unchaste).

CAUTION! IT'S A JUNGLE OUT THERE!

In the puzzle you must find and circle 10 things that will keep you out of the quicksand (Satan's traps) and on the right trail (chastity) in your journey through the jungle (world). If you stumble into the quicksand, cross out the word before you start to sink! The word or word groups are read from left to right or backwards, right to left.

```
Z Z Z Z Z Z N O I T A B R U T S A M
Z Z G R O U P A C T I V I T I E S Z
Z G N I K C E N S E K O J Y T R I D
Z Z Z L E S N U O C O T N E T S I L
Z S T A Y I N G O U T L A T E Z Z Z
Z C I S U M G N I T F I L P U Z Z Z
Z Z V I R T U O U S T H O U G H T S
P E T T I N G Y H P A R G O N R O P
Z Z I M P U R E T H O U G H T S Z Z
Z Z Y T S E D O M M I Z R E Y A R P
Z Z Z Z Z Z N O I T A C I N R O F
Z Z Z P I H S D N E I R F E U R T Z
Z S C R I P T U R E R E A D I N G Z
Z Z Z Z H O M O S E X U A L I T Y
    Z O N Y A S O T E G A R U O C
    Z Z Z C L E A N S P E A C H Z
    C I S U M E V I T S E G G U S
Z Z Z O B E Y P A R E N T S Z Z Z Z
Z R R A T E D M O V I E S Z Z Z Z Z
```

Lesson 34 — Obedience: I Will Hold Fast to the Lord's Standards
(Hold Fast Word Find)

PREPARATION: Review questionnaire discussion (p. 132-133) and quotation (p. 133) in *Young Women Manual 2.*

TO MAKE ACTIVITY HANDOUT: *Copy and color the *Hold Fast Word Find* (p. 82) for each young woman.

LESSON MATCH ACTIVITY—*Hold Fast Word Find*: Help young women realize the importance of holding fast to the Lord's standards. Read the quote by Spencer W. Kimball on the word find (shown right). Have young women fill in the missing word to identify ways they can hold fast to the Lord's standards.

COLOR FLORAL SYMBOL:

*Color floral symbol on activity and scripture card. File activity in Young Women "Value-able" Journal behind the value tab.

> *Choice & Accountability*
> *(orange poppy)*

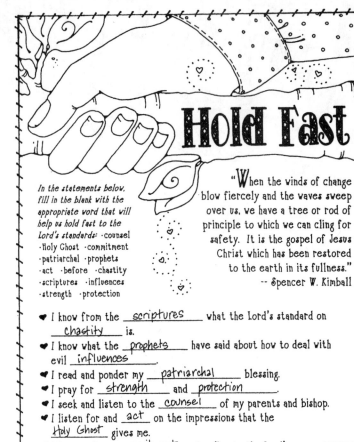

Hold Fast

In the statements below, fill in the blank with the appropriate word that will help us hold fast to the Lord's standards: ·counsel ·Holy Ghost ·commitment ·patriarchal ·prophets ·act ·before ·chastity ·scriptures ·influences ·strength ·protection

"When the winds of change blow fiercely and the waves sweep over us, we have a tree or rod of principle to which we can cling for safety. It is the gospel of Jesus Christ which has been restored to the earth in its fullness."
-- Spencer W. Kimball

❤ I know from the __scriptures__ what the Lord's standard on __chastity__ is.
❤ I know what the __prophets__ have said about how to deal with evil __influences__.
❤ I read and ponder my __patriarchal__ blessing.
❤ I pray for __strength__ and __protection__.
❤ I seek and listen to the __counsel__ of my parents and bishop.
❤ I listen for and __act__ on the impressions that the __Holy Ghost__ gives me.
❤ I have made a __commitment__ to cling to the Lord's standard __before__ I am faced with temptation.

MIDWEEK ACTIVITY:

Make Some Obedience Cookies:
Choose a terrific cookie recipe and make it with the young women. Follow the recipe exactly and bake.

Make Some Disobedience Cookies:
With the same recipe omit the sugar and salt or the baking soda or half the flavoring or sweet ingredients, e.g., vanilla, or chocolate chips. Bake and keep separate from the Obedience Cookies (detailed above).

Discuss the Difference:
Have a discussion around the table with milk and one each of the Obedience Cookies and Disobedience Cookies. Talk about what can happen in life if you choose not to obey certain commandments. Life can be sweet and full, or it may lack certain wonderful ingredients. As the Spirit directs, choose some scriptures to make the point. Bear testimony.

Hold Fast

In the statements below, fill in the blank with the appropriate word that will help us hold fast to the Lord's standards: ·counsel ·Holy Ghost ·commitment ·patriarchal ·prophets ·act ·before ·chastity ·scriptures ·influences ·strength ·protection

"When the winds of change blow fiercely and the waves sweep over us, we have a tree or rod of principle to which we can cling for safety. It is the gospel of Jesus Christ which has been restored to the earth in its fullness."
-- Spencer W. Kimball

- ❤ I know from the _____ what the Lord's standard on _____ is.
- ❤ I know what the _____ have said about how to deal with evil _____.
- ❤ I read and ponder my _____ blessing.
- ❤ I pray for _____ and _____.
- ❤ I seek and listen to the _____ of my parents and bishop.
- ❤ I listen for and _____ on the impressions that the _____ gives me.
- ❤ I have made a _____ to cling to the Lord's standard _____ I am faced with temptation.

Lesson 35	Choices: I Will Make Wise Choices
	(Thumbs up—Thumbs Down Choices Game)

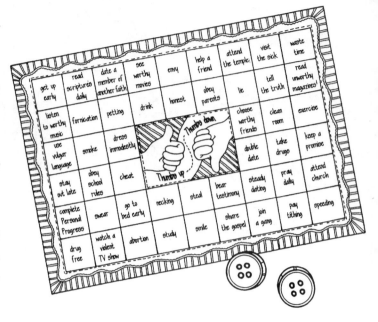

PREPARATION: Review chalkboard discussion (p. 134-135) in *Young Women Manual 2*.

TO MAKE ACTIVITY HANDOUT: *Copy, color, and cut out *Thumbs Up—Thumbs Down Choices Game* (p. 84) for each young woman. Supply a button or penny marker for each.

LESSON MATCH ACTIVITY—*Thumbs Up—Thumbs Down Choices Game*: Help young women understand that the consequences of their actions are not always immediate but they can affect them throughout their lives. With this game young women vote if the choices are right or wrong and tell consequences for making each choice.

To Play:

1. Lay game board on a flat surface.

2. Have young women take turns throwing a button or penny onto the game board.

3. When the button or penny lands on a choice, have all young women say, or show thumbs up, if the choice is right and thumbs down if the choice is wrong.

4. Have the person who tossed the button or penny tell a good or bad consequence for making that good or bad choice.

5. Keep playing until the time is up (15 minutes).

6. Ask young women to take the game home to share with their family.

COLOR FLORAL SYMBOL:

*Color floral symbol on activity and scripture card. File activity in Young Women "Value-able" Journal behind the value tab.

Choice & Accountability (orange poppy)

MIDWEEK ACTIVITY:

Future Focus:

Project young women into the future with the choices they could make, e.g., live your life with the end in mind.

1. Have them ponder these questions: Where will I be if . . . ?, how will I look if . . . ?, and what will I be if . . . ?

Ask questions: Do we marry the people we date?

Project into the Future with These Situations:

 - You choose to marry someone of another faith.
 - You choose to marry an active member.
 - You choose to marry a less-active member.
 - What if you don't live the Word of Wisdom?
 - What will your life be like if you wear immodest clothing?

2. Try to see the end result of choices. Tell them that when you pick up a stick the other end comes with it.

3. Read Alma 48:11-18 (a description of a future companion). Keep in mind that young women should achieve these traits as well if they are to attract a future companion they admire.

4. Have people who have experienced good and bad choices talk to them.

waste time	visit the sick	attend the temple	help a friend	envy	see worthy movies
read unworthy magazines	tell the truth	lie	obey parents	be honest	drink
exercise	clean room	choose worthy friends			
keep a promise	take drugs	double date	bear testimony	steal	necking
attend church	pray daily	steady dating	share the gospel	smile	study
speeding	pay tithing	join a gang			

Thumbs down

Thumbs up

date a member of another faith	read scriptures daily	get up early
petting	fornication	listen to worthy music
dress immodestly	smoke	use vulgar language
cheat	obey school rules	stay out late
go to bed early	swear	complete Personal Progress
abortion	watch a violent TV show	drug free

Lesson 36 — Honesty: I Will Be Honest with Myself and Others
(I'm "Sew" Honest! Stand-up Card)

In honesty, I measure up!

The blessings I receive from being honest are:

PREPARATION: Review quotation (p. 140) in *Young Women Manual 2*.

TO MAKE ACTIVITY HANDOUT: *Copy *I'm "Sew" Honest! Stand-up Card* (p. 86) on cardstock paper for each young woman.

LESSON MATCH ACTIVITY—*I'm "Sew" Honest! Stand-up Card*: Help young women write on the card the blessings they receive from being honest. *Ideas:* Peace of mind, self-respect, others trust them, they don't have to remember what they said or did, they have a clear conscience/not burdened with guilt.

COLOR SYMBOL:
*Color floral symbol on activity and scripture card. File activity in Young Women "Value-able" Journal behind the value tab.

Integrity (purple pansy)

MIDWEEK ACTIVITIES:

Malt Shop Honesty Test:
Treat young women to a malt or milkshake. Tell the owner or cashier ahead of time that you are teaching a lesson on honesty. Have them charge you for one less item (e.g., seven malts when eight malts were served). Pay for your order, then check the bill after you leave. Tell the girls they made a mistake and only charged you for seven. Some will suggest going back to pay, some may say it's not worth the trouble. Then go back and make up the difference.

Honest Reflection:
Ask the young women to think about who's cheating who when we are dishonest?
Step 1: Show a thin piece of fabric and talk about the veil that separates us from heaven. We have to live by faith, not seeing on the other side of the veil, but Heavenly Father knows our every thought and action. He knows the truth of all the things we think and do.

Step 2: Ask young women to quietly reflect on their past thoughts and actions regarding honesty at home, school, and in the community. Ask them to think: Do I cheat? Do I steal? Do I gossip?
Step 3: Discuss types of honesty. Some people don't feel it is dishonest when they copy a video that says no copying allowed or copy a song or a computer program; when they gossip; when they say they will call a friend even though they don't intend to; when they accept a date even though they aren't sixteen yet, or say they are older than they are; or accept a date when the don't really want to date the guy; when they say they paid a fine and they didn't; or steal another person's time by being late.
Step 4: Talk about feelings you have when you are dishonest. Say that honesty builds strength, and dishonesty breeds mistrust of others, dislike of self, feelings of sadness.
Step 5: Show the thin fabric again and ask, "Do you feel from your actions that you are now worthy to pass through the veil and enter into God's presence?"

Lesson 37 Chastity: I Will Maintain Virtue Through Righteous Living
(Painting Righteous Habits Planner)

PREPARATION: Review lesson application activity (p. 144) in *Young Women Manual 2*.

TO MAKE ACTIVITY HANDOUT: *Copy and color the *Painting Righteous Habits Planner* (p. 88) for each young woman.

1. Color planner in the seven young women colors: Faith (white), Divine Nature (blue), Individual Worth (red), Knowledge (green) Choice and Accountability (orange), Good Works (yellow), and Integrity (purple).

2. Tell young women that they can color their world with beautiful thoughts, words, and deeds, painting righteous habits daily.

3. Have young women write in the squares next to each value how they will use that value to live the law of chastity.

LESSON MATCH ACTIVITY—*Painting Righteous Habits Planner*: Have young women write what they consider righteous habits.

COLOR FLORAL SYMBOL:
*Color floral symbol on activity and scripture card. File activity in Young Women "Value-able" Journal behind the value tab.

Choice & Accountability (orange poppy)

MIDWEEK ACTIVITIES:

Choice of Oreo Cookies or a Banquet:
Prepare ahead of time a banquet of delightful food, e.g., pizza, salad, and apple pie, and place under a tablecloth. Place a plate of Oreo cookies on top of the tablecloth. Tell young women that they can have an Oreo cookie *now* or wait for the treat that is under the tablecloth. Hint that what is under the tablecloth is much better than an Oreo, but they have to trust you. We have to trust our leaders, parents, etc., that saving intimacy until after marriage is a treat worth waiting for. After a while uncover the tablecloth to serve young women the banquet (but not the Oreos). Then after they eat, take the Oreo cookies and crush them in front of them telling them that Satan

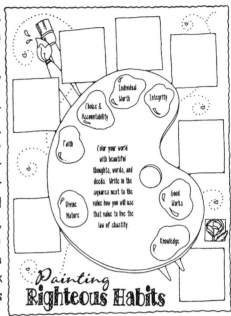

Painting
Righteous Habits

wants you to be satisfied with immediate pleasure, e.g., the Oreo cookies, but it doesn't last. Heavenly Father wants us to wait for the banquet (having a sacred and eternal love), the relationship that is worth waiting for. Talk about Satan's temptations.

Observing Only the Packaging Can Be Deceiving:
Have a panel discussion and talk about meeting a guy with a testimony or a guy who is good-looking. Some have a testimony and some do not. Have priesthood leaders choose young men for the panels. Direct questions to the panel to learn how young women can bring out the spiritual side of a guy and learn what he is really like. Questions: How can a girl tell if he is going to treat her with respect and love? How can she tell if he likes her for her good qualities and her testimony? How can a girl say no and still keep a guy's friendship? What are the qualities a girl should look for that are deeper than the outward appearance? How can she find or bring out these qualities if he doesn't yet have them?) Continue with activity below.

Object Lesson: Before or after the activity when the young men are gone, do the following object lesson. Have young women unwrap some gifts. Wrap the fancy gifts in plain paper and the plain gifts in fancy paper, e.g., an old shoe in a fancy package, and a temple recommend in the plain package, a *TV Guide* in a fancy package and a *New Era* magazine in the plain. Compare these with a guy who is not particularly handsome to them but could have great qualities they want eternally. Also explain that, often, good on the outside can be good on the inside too.

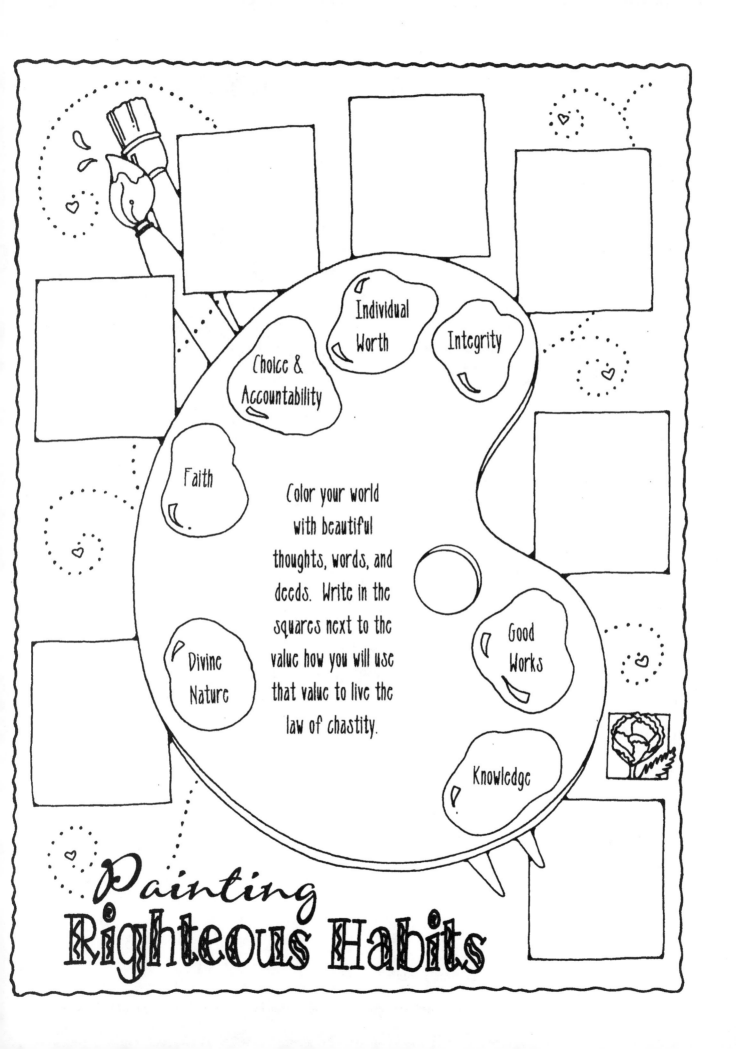

Individual Worth

Integrity

Choice & Accountability

Faith

Color your world with beautiful thoughts, words, and deeds. Write in the squares next to the value how you will use that value to live the law of chastity.

Good Works

Divine Nature

Knowledge

Painting
Righteous Habits

Lesson 38 Physical Health: I Will Maintain My Physical Health

(You Deserve a Hand! Health Chart)

PREPARATION: Review teacher presentation (p. 146-147) in *Young Women Manual 2.*

TO MAKE ACTIVITY HANDOUT: *Copy and color the *You Deserve a Hand! Health Chart* (p. 90) for each young woman.

LESSON MATCH ACTIVITY—*You Deserve a Hand! Health Chart:* Tell young women that the health habits you acquire early in life will either increase or decrease your energy in the future. With good health we can fulfill our earthly mission. Read the message on the hand which explains that each of the five health needs are vital to each other (e.g., we can't exercise effectively if we haven't eaten a balanced diet).

Encourage young women to chart their success this next week in these five areas (found on the fingers): Exercise, Balanced Diet, Water, Clean and Well Groomed, and Rest. Tell them if they care for their body in this way, they deserve a hand!

COLOR FLORAL SYMBOL:
*Color floral symbol on activity and scripture card. File activity in Young Women "Value-able" Journal behind the value tab.

Choice & Accountability (orange poppy)

MIDWEEK ACTIVITIES:

1. **Aerobics class.**
2. **Walking.**
3. **Volleyball or basketball.**
4. **Bike riding in the park with a picnic.**
5. **Fitness field instruction.** Go to a nearby college and have someone in the fitness field talk to the young women about fitness careers.
6. **Salad bar discussion.** As a group, enjoy eating a variety of delicious healthy salad greens as you talk about a basic desire for good health. Ask young women if our hearts are set on looking good and feeling good, or just looking good through up-to-date fashion and stylish hair. Looking good comes from within by eating right, getting enough

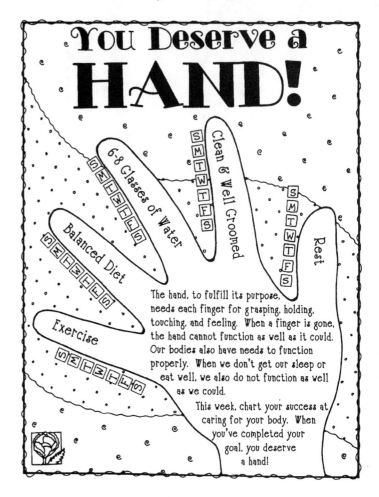

You Deserve a HAND!

6-8 Glasses of Water SMTWTFS
Clean & Well Groomed SMTWTFS
Balanced Diet SMTWTFS
Rest SMTWTFS
Exercise SMTWTFS

The hand, to fulfill its purpose, needs each finger for grasping, holding, touching, and feeling. When a finger is gone, the hand cannot function as well as it could. Our bodies also have needs to function properly. When we don't get our sleep or eat well, we also do not function as well as we could.

This week, chart your success at caring for your body. When you've completed your goal, you deserve a hand!

sleep, and getting the right amount of exercise and fresh air. Take a daily walk with a family member or friends. Start out by walking fifteen minutes one direction and fifteen back, then increase it until you've had a good brisk walk each day in the fresh air. Review these quotes by athletes: "Activity stimulates; it doesn't tire you." "Use it or lose it." "A minute on the lips, a month on the hips." Talk about sharpening the saw (even demonstrating this). Sharpening the saw is to go the extra mile (to look and feel your best).

7. **Grooming demonstration** on personal care, makeup, hair, manicure, cleanliness, etc.
8. **Healthy shake demonstration** and tasting table.
9. **Have a licensed nutritionist talk.**

You Deserve a HAND!

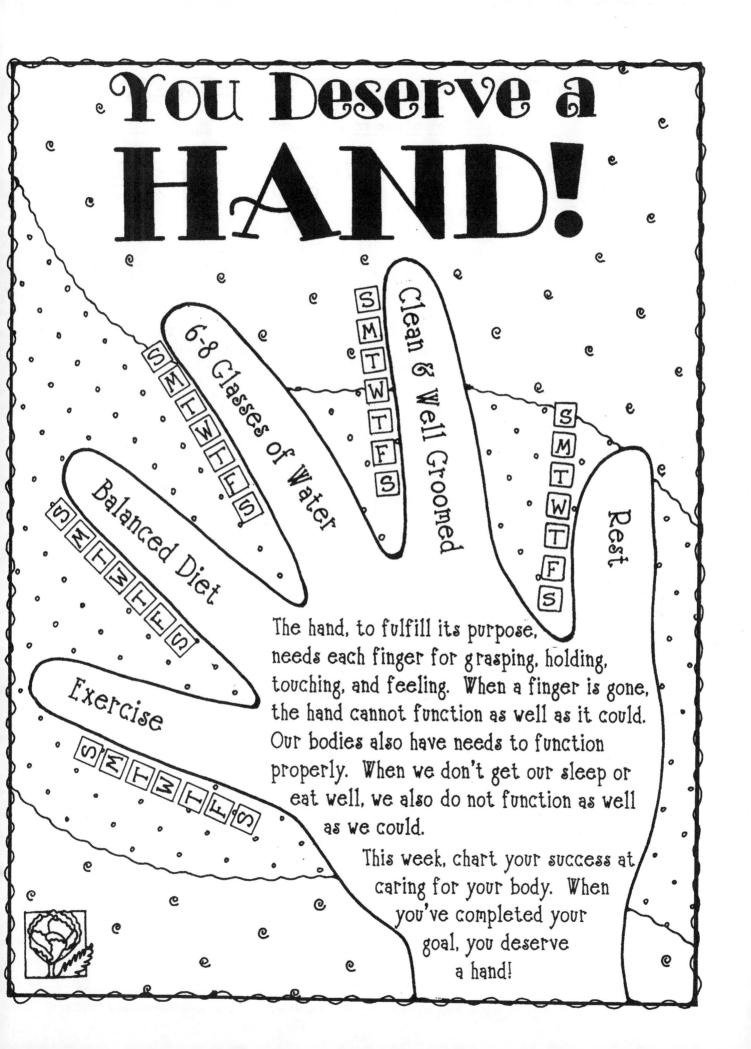

6-8 Glasses of Water

Clean & Well Groomed

Balanced Diet

Rest

Exercise

The hand, to fulfill its purpose, needs each finger for grasping, holding, touching, and feeling. When a finger is gone, the hand cannot function as well as it could. Our bodies also have needs to function properly. When we don't get our sleep or eat well, we also do not function as well as we could.

This week, chart your success at caring for your body. When you've completed your goal, you deserve a hand!

Lesson 39 Physical Health: I Will Learn How to Prevent Disease

(Be Free of Disease! Unseen Fiend Find)

PREPARATION: Review chalkboard discussion (p. 150) in *Young Women Manual 2*.

TO MAKE ACTIVITY HANDOUT: *Copy and color the *Be Free of Disease! Unseen Fiend Find* (p. 92) for each young woman.

ACTIVITY—*Be Free of Disease! Unseen Fiend Find*: Discuss with young women ways to prevent the spread of disease-causing microorganisms and reasons it is important with this Be Free of Disease! unseen fiend find.

To Do Puzzle: Discover 11 ways to keep those unseen fiends from causing you problems! Write your answers in the border (answers below).

Answers: (1) Clean the house regularly. (2) Protect food by keeping it covered and refrigerated. (3) Wash food. (4) Wash hands. (5) Brush teeth to prevent decay. (6) Cover mouth when sneezing or coughing. (7) Protect your feet from germs in the ground. (8) Eat properly and get enough rest. (9) Make sure milk, water, and food are safe to eat. (10) Immunize. (11) Obey the law of chastity.

Be Free of Disease!

Discover 11 ways to keep those unseen fiends from causing you problems! Write your answers in the border.

If you can't see this sign, you're too close!

Milk Water

A-A-Achoo!

COLOR FLORAL SYMBOL:
*Color floral symbol on activity and scripture card. File activity in Young Women "Value-able" Journal behind the value tab.

Knowledge (green ivy)

MIDWEEK ACTIVITIES:

Guest Speaker:

Have guest speakers come who have lost loved ones or close friends to cancer, emphysema, AIDS, liver disease, heart attack, stroke, etc. They can share what it was like to see their loved ones in their condition. Talk about their experiences as they assisted them and saw someone care for them. Talk about what might have been done to prevent the illness. Was it genetic? What could have been done to avoid the illness? Talk about ways to prevent disease through diet, exercise, mental and spiritual wellness, etc.

Tasting Table Talk:

Have young women each bring a food item and tell how it nourishes the body. Place these on a tasting table with cards that show what they do, e.g., "Carrots are good for the eyes. They help prevent night blindness." Visit a produce department of a grocery store that has an educational program on nutritious foods so young women can learn about fruits and vegetables and how to prepare them. Elementary schools often go to stores on field trips, and some companies, like Dole Pineapple, sponsor these kinds of programs. You could also ask your Relief Society enrichment leaders to give a demonstration on nutritious food, or a representative from the 4-H or a government agency could provide a demo.

Lesson 40 — Self-Mastery: I Will Strengthen My Character
(Harvesting My Destiny Garden)

PREPARATION: Review fill-in-the-blank (p. 154) and writing activity (p. 155) in *Young Women Manual 2*.

TO MAKE ACTIVITY HANDOUT: *Copy and color the *Harvesting My Destiny Garden* (p. 94) for each young woman.

LESSON MATCH ACTIVITY—*Harvesting My Destiny Garden*: Help young women learn that by planting three tiny seeds of thought, she can overcome three bad habits and reap a harvest of good habits that will determine her eternal destiny.

1. Write three bad habits you wish to change on the form, e.g., lazy, selfish, bad moods.

2. Sow a good thought. Below the bad habit, write a positive thought that will change the bad habit (e.g., if the habit is "laziness," write "I like to work," or if the habit is "selfishness," write, "I will think of others," or if the habit is "bad moods," write, "I will think happy thoughts."

3. Harvest Your Destiny Garden: Write what each thought reaps (action, habit, character, and destiny).

COLOR FLORAL SYMBOL:
*Color floral symbol on activity and scripture card. File activity in Young Women "Value-able" Journal behind the value tab.

Integrity (purple pansy)

MIDWEEK ACTIVITY:
Apple Pie Positive Self-Talk Seminar:
Be prepared to show young women an apple and a fresh apple pie (hopefully one that is warm fresh out of the oven). Tell young women that it is easy to be just an apple, but with a little more effort we can be an apple pie. As we know, we are all children of God; we have the desire to be better. [Leader: You may want to demonstrate how to make an apple pie.] To become an apple pie we must add the sugar and butter to make caramel syrup. We add the spices and a rich tasty crust. Self-mastery is like

that. You can take you the way you are (show the apple) or we can add the things that make you even better than you are now (show the apple pie). Don't be afraid to tell yourself that you are of great worth and value. Add spice to your life by strengthening your character. List "Apple"ing Character Traits on the board.

Step 1: Have guest speakers come prepared to speak (see 3 below). Provide notepaper and pencils for young women with an apple and apple-pie sticker.

Step 2: Ahead of time put up positive self-talk signs in the shapes of apples all over the room on the floor, ceiling, walls, table, light, and board. *Ideas:* "You're the apple of Heavenly Father's eye." "Bloom where you're planted," "Confidence is a gift you can give yourself," "Practice releases pressure," "If it is to be, it is up to me," "Nothing is too good to be true, nothing is too good to last," "Do your best and leave the rest," "Count to 10 and then start over again," "If at first you don't succeed . . . try, try again."

Step 3: Have a guest speaker tell how the girls can make their life into an apple pie through building their character.

   Ideas: (1) Describe good self-talk and bad self-talk. Talk about what positive self-talk can do.

   (2) Search the scriptures to find the right and wrong way to care for yourself, e.g., the Word of Wisdom, commandments like fasting and exercising.

Step 4: Have young women list five self-talk messages they wish to take home and memorize.

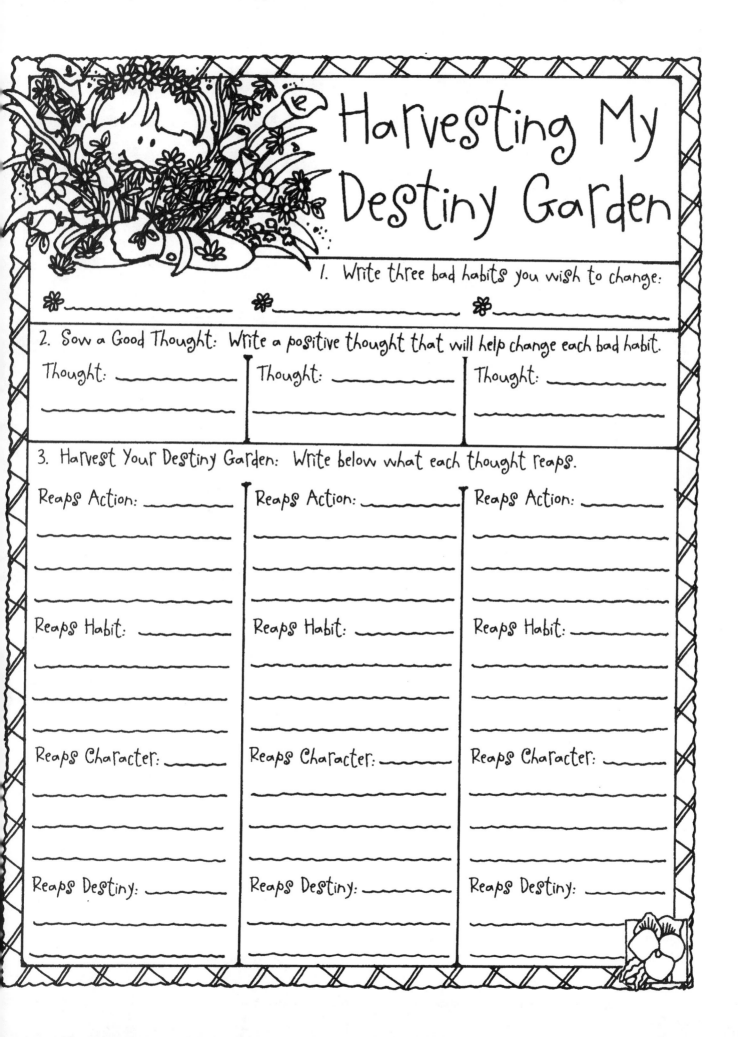

Harvesting My Destiny Garden

1. Write three bad habits you wish to change:

❀ _____ ❀ _____ ❀ _____

2. Sow a Good Thought: Write a positive thought that will help change each bad habit.

| Thought: _____ | Thought: _____ | Thought: _____ |
| _____ | _____ | _____ |

3. Harvest Your Destiny Garden: Write below what each thought reaps.

Reaps Action: _____	Reaps Action: _____	Reaps Action: _____
_____	_____	_____
_____	_____	_____
_____	_____	_____
Reaps Habit: _____	Reaps Habit: _____	Reaps Habit: _____
_____	_____	_____
_____	_____	_____
_____	_____	_____
Reaps Character: _____	Reaps Character: _____	Reaps Character: _____
_____	_____	_____
_____	_____	_____
_____	_____	_____
Reaps Destiny: _____	Reaps Destiny: _____	Reaps Destiny: _____
_____	_____	_____

Lesson 41 — Optimism: I Will Develop a Cheerful, Optimistic Attitude
(Cup Full of Cheerful Thoughts)

PREPARATION: Review lesson application (p. 160) in *Young Women Manual 2*.

TO MAKE ACTIVITY HANDOUT: *Copy *Cheerful Cup* label and cards (p. 96) for each young woman. Glue label on a paper cup and fill with lemon head candies.

LESSON MATCH ACTIVITY—*Cup Full of Cheerful Thoughts*:
Step 1: Talk about the storms in life, things we face and how we can change our attitude to create sunny days. Share the following quote:

>   *"Stop seeking out the storms and
>   enjoy more fully the sunlight."*
> - President Gordon B. Hinckley, April 1986 *Ensign*
>   (First Presidency Message)

Step 2: Help young women memorize the poem by Emily Dickinson found on the cup label. Talk about the difference in people's attitude and how it affects their lives in all areas.
Read the lemon sign on the cup label: "Don't wear a sour face—smile, smile, smile!" Tell young women not to be a lemon head and smile.
Option: Instead of lemon heads (or before you put lemon heads in the cup), fill it half full of lemonade. Say, "An optimist says the cup is half full where a pessimist says the cup is half empty." While girls drink their lemonade ask them, which will you be?

COLOR FLORAL SYMBOL:
*Color floral symbol on activity and scripture card. File activity in Young Women "Value-able" Journal behind the value tab.

> *Choice & Accountability (orange poppy)*

MIDWEEK ACTIVITY:

Positive Thought Scripture Scramble:
Have young women compete in two teams to race through the Topical Guide and Index of the scriptures to find ideas on how they can be more positive. Time young women, giving them thirty minutes to come up with motivational scriptures. Have them take turns reading a scripture showing to be positive. Keep score on the chalkboard of the two teams. If the other team has the same scripture give both teams the point. The teams with the most "get positive" scriptures wins!
Subject Ideas: Abstain, abound, abundance, abundant life, abundantly, accept, acceptable, accountability, affection, agency, etc. For example in the Topical Guide you will find the word *alive* and the scripture reference "even so in Christ shall all be made alive" (1 Corinthians 15:2). The young women don't need to look up the scripture, just write the reference from the description.
Summary: After they have shared their ideas, say, "The scriptures have so many positive thoughts to encourage us each day. The more we search them, the more we will have a cheerful optimistic attitude and the happier we will be."

If the
grass looks
greener
on the
other
side...

...fertilize!

When
life gives
you
lemons,
make
lemonade!

Smile and
the world
smiles
with you,
cry and
your
mascara
runs!

A merry
heart
maketh a
cheerful
countenance.

Proverbs
15:13

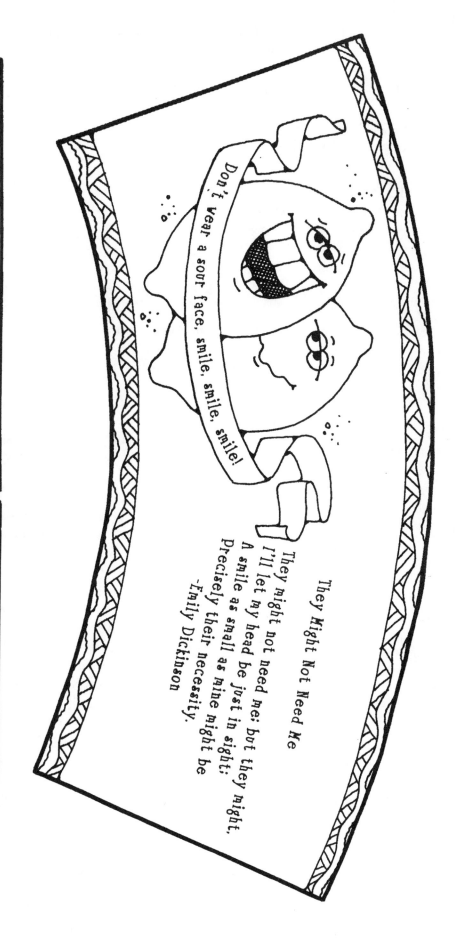

Don't wear a sour face, smile, smile, smile!

They Might Not Need Me

They might not need me;
I'll let my head be just in sight;
A smile as small as mine might be
Precisely their necessity.

-Emily Dickinson

Lesson 42	Gratitude: I Will Express Appreciation
	(Gratitude Card and Grateful Heart! Bookmark)

PREPARATION: Review Preparation 2 (page 161) and Conclusion Handout (page 164) in *Young Women Manual 2.*

TO MAKE ACTIVITY HANDOUT: *Copy, color, and cut out the *Gratitude Card* and *Grateful Heart! Bookmark* (p. 98-99) for each young woman. Fold envelope and glue flaps. Fold the card and glue the "shine brighter because of you" label on the card.

LESSON MATCH ACTIVITY—*Gratitude Card and Grateful Heart! Bookmark*: Give each young woman a bookmark to place in her scriptures to remind her to express gratitude toward others. Also give young women a card they can give to someone to show their gratitude. Have young women write a special note of thanks, slip it in the envelope, address it and deliver or send.

COLOR FLORAL SYMBOL:
*Color floral symbol on activity and scripture card. File activity in Young Women "Value-able" Journal behind the value tab.

Choice & Accountability (orange poppy)

MIDWEEK ACTIVITY:

Express Gratitude with a Mighty Change of Heart Marathon: For more information, see "The Scriptures Teach Us How Our Hearts Can Be Changed" scripture discussion and review (p. 105) in *Young Women Manual 3.*

Step 1: Ahead of time, make a large sign inside of a heart: "Mighty Change of Heart Marathon" and write the scripture Alma 5:14 in a large banner with large letters that stretch across the room as follows: *"Have you spiritually been born of God? Have ye received his image in your countenances? Have ye experienced this mighty change in your hearts."* Write out thirty situations on slips of paper and place them in a bowl (across the room). Post two signs, *Christlike* and *Not Christlike.* Place two tape dispensers near the bowl.

Step 2: As the activity begins, discuss this change of heart where we receive the image of God in our countenance (read Alma 5:14 from the banner).

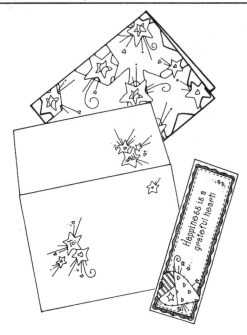

Discuss how we can express thanks to Heavenly Father by our actions for what He has done for us. Talk about repentance, which represents a change of heart, so we can have His image in our countenance and find peace and happiness as we become more Christlike.

Step 3: Divide young women into teams and line up on the other side of the room opposite of the signs and bowl. Have them compete at the word "go" to race across the room, draw from the bowl a situation, read it silently, and post it with a piece of tape under the sign *Christlike* or *Not Christlike.* The first team to complete wins!

Step 4: Place chairs near the signs and situations and have a discussion, reading the situations aloud, checking them for accuracy, discussing the actions.

Step 5: Award young women with a Church video that reflects a mighty change of heart. Serve heart-shaped treats, e.g., sandwiches cut into hearts, heart-shaped cookies, or Jell-O blocks cookie-cutter cut-outs.

Step 6: Give young women the following message written on a large red heart to hang in their room:

My Change of Heart
I will learn about Christ and His commandments.
I will have faith in Christ and believe in His Atonement. I will ask for forgiveness, and be forgiven through the Lord's mercy. I will make a covenant to keep the commandments, and do good all my days.

(see Mosiah 5:2, 5)

From the heart

Happiness is a grateful heart!

The stars
shine brighter
because of you!

Thanks so much!

Paste on
inside of
card

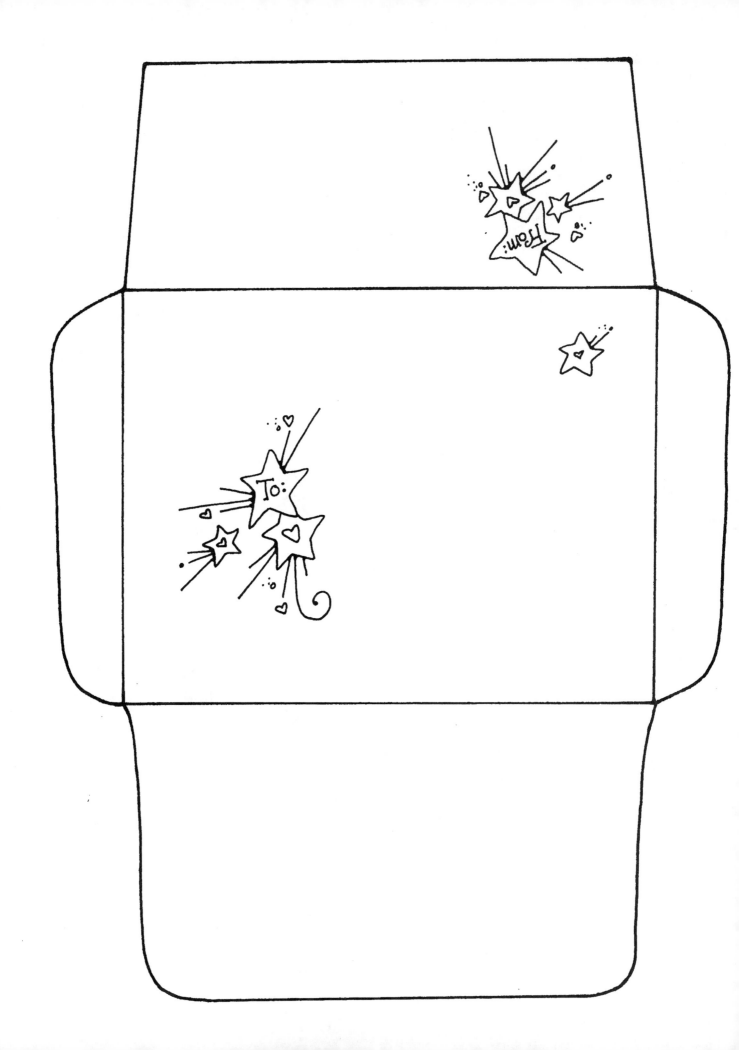

Lesson 43	Management: I Will Use My Time Wisely
	(My Ant Farm Leisure Time Log)

PREPARATION: Review chalkboard discussion 1-7 (p. 167-168) and lesson application (p. 168) in *Young Women Manual 2.*

TO MAKE ACTIVITY HANDOUT: *Copy and cut out the *My Ant Farm Leisure Time Log* (p. 101) for each young woman.

LESSON MATCH ACTIVITY—*My Ant Farm Leisure Time Log*: Tell young women, "Eternity is won or lost in our leisure time." Young women can record activities on this log that are a wise use of time. Then in their free (leisure) time they can do these things. Have young women study the ideas, circle those they want to do in the next few months, and add to the list as they think up other leisure-time activities. Have them schedule chosen activities during their free time. This way they will have something to do and have something to look forward to each day. Talk about "dovetailing" activities (doing two things at once).

Dovetail Ideas:

· *While talking on the phone:* mend or sort socks, iron clothes, wash the dishes, or clean your room.

· *During the television ads:* do your nails, put on a face mask, read, exercise, drink water, or memorize notes for a quiz.

· *While doing homework:* drink plenty of water and eat an apple or healthy snacks.

· *While cleaning or driving:* listen to church music, scriptures or books on tape, or practice singing.

· *Memorize test material:* by placing test material on cards or a cassette tape ahead of time you can memorize your notes while you put on makeup, blow-dry your hair, wait for your nails to dry, wash the dishes, do household chores, or wait for a friend.

COLOR FLORAL SYMBOL:
*Color floral symbol on activity and scripture card. File activity in Young Women "Value-able" Journal behind the value tab.

Choice & Accountability (orange poppy)

MIDWEEK ACTIVITY:

Leisure Picnic to Talk About Leisure Time:
Have a picnic indoors or outdoors. Call ahead and ask every young woman and leader to bring: (1) a sack lunch, (2) a blanket, and (3) ideas to share of leisure-time productive activities and leisure-time—time-wasting activities. Decorate by enlarging drawings of ants and placing one on each blanket. Talk about industrious ants and how they don't waste their leisure time. Have each young woman and the leaders stand up and share their ideas.

My Ant Farm
Leisure Time Log

Don't sit around like a bump on a log! Follow the example of the industrious ants and schedule your free time using the ideas below:

- Develop a talent
- Meditate
- Play family games
- Read scriptures
- Learn to play a musical instrument
- Give a manicure
- Do crafts
- Do genealogy
- Visit the sick or sad
- Play sports

- Do gardening
- Take a nature walk
- Help a neighbor
- Write in journal
- Watch educational program
- Plan a party
- Read a book
- Achieve Personal Progress goals
- Make a scrapbook

Other leisure time ideas:

- _____
- _____
- _____
- _____
- _____

- _____
- _____
- _____
- _____
- _____

Lesson 44	Talents: I Will Develop My Talents
	(My Basket Full of Talents! Talented Egg Show)

PREPARATION: Review lesson application (p. 171) in *Young Women Manual 2*.

TO MAKE ACTIVITY HANDOUT: *Copy, color, and cut out the *Talents* basket and egg cards on cardstock paper for each young woman. Cut a slit at the top of the basket inside (leaving the background inside and outside the basket). Fold the egg cards in half, gluing back to back.

LESSON MATCH ACTIVITY— *My Basket Full of Talents Talented Egg Show*: Tell young women that their "life's basket" is like a basket that can be filled with talents, but we must work to develop them. Heavenly Father has given us the potential to develop nearly any talent we wish. We can choose what we put in our basket of talents. So let's be a "good egg" and develop our talents.

Ahead of time: interview parents and write on at least three of the talented egg cards the obvious talents each young woman has.

During the activity: young women could also help name obvious talents the other young women have. With the rest of the talented egg cards, have the young women write talents they wish to acquire and ways to develop the talents.

COLOR FLORAL SYMBOL:

*Color floral symbol on activity and scripture card. File activity in Young Women ""Value-able"" Journal behind the value tab.

Individual Worth (red rose)

MIDWEEK ACTIVITIES:

Parable of the Talents Talent Night:
Have a talent night and invite the parents.
Ideas:
1. Review the Parable of the Talents. Use coins for

theme decorations and give refreshments with a gold coin (chocolate candy wrapped in gold paper).

2. Play oldies songs and have girls do a lip sync with it. You could assign two songs to each class and invite the parents, and even the bishopric and Young Women leaders, to join you.

3. Do a few musical numbers.

4. Model clothing someone has made.

5. Display artwork.

6. Do a variety of readings.

7. Give young women a pretty piece of paper and a pencil to write down talents they wish to develop.

8. Talk about various talents, and have a speaker or two tell briefly how they developed their talent.

9. Tell of the 1% inspiration and 99% perspiration theory—that talents take time and effort.

10. Take young women on a "talent trek" across the room. Mark a talent trail with crepe paper taped to the floor to mark the path to talents displayed.

Talent Tasting Table. Have young women volunteer to bring casseroles, salads, or desserts they make themselves. Ask someone to gather and type up the recipes and have them ready.

Lesson 45 — Cultural Arts: Cultural Arts Participation
(I Love Cultural Arts! Frame/Journal Page)

PREPARATION: Review discussion (p. 173) in *Young Women Manual 2*.

TO MAKE ACTIVITY HANDOUT: *Copy and color the *I Love Cultural Arts! Frame/Journal Page* (p. 106) for each young woman.

LESSON MATCH ACTIVITY—*I Love Cultural Arts! Frame/Journal Page*: Review the 13th Article of Faith and ask young women to think of ways they can add to their life and to the lives of children through cultural arts. Many of these ideas are found in the frame/journal page. Have young women refer to the pictures on the frame as they plan cultural arts activities. Encourage them to take a photo of themselves or draw a picture of themselves participating in a cultural arts activity and record their cultural arts experiences next to the picture on the journal page. They could also save tickets and programs for special events to place in their journal.

COLOR FLORAL SYMBOL:

*Color floral symbol on activity and scripture card. File activity in Young Women "Value-able" Journal behind the value tab.

Knowledge (green ivy)

MIDWEEK ACTIVITIES:
Museum Show-and-Tell:

At a museum divide young women into groups to scope out the museum in sections. Then get together and have young women show and tell about what they have learned, being the tour guides for their portion of the museum. Take photos to place on the *I Love Cultural Arts!* frame/journal page (above) and write about your findings and experience.

Teach Dance Steps:

Have someone come and teach the basics: ballet, western swing, line dancing, square dancing, folk dance, ballroom, disco, break dancing, and more.

Have a Casual Talent Night:

Find an interest or talent from each girl to spotlight. Have young women share their talents, e.g., piano, flute, guitar, craft skill, cooking demos, singing, scrapbooks, crafts. Display items made and have them tell about their hobbies and interests and how they got started.

Soap Carving: Have each young woman carve their own bar of soap into a sculpture they can place in their bathroom.

Old Movie Night:

Bring a favorite movie to share or enjoy an animated movie together.

Go to a local play.

Put on a play for the next ward party.

I ♥ the Cultural Arts!

Lesson 46	Finances: I Will Learn to Be Financially Responsible
	(Money Mottos to Place in Wallet)

PREPARATION: Review discussion (p. 176) and conclusion (p. 177) in *Young Women Manual 2.*

TO MAKE ACTIVITY HANDOUT (BILL): *Copy, color, and cut out the *Think Before I Spend* bill (p. 108) for each young woman. Have them write their money goals on the bill and fold and glue it back-to-back. Laminate.

TO MAKE ACTIVITY HANDOUT (CREDIT CARD): *Copy, color, and cut out the *Do Not Forget . . . Stay out of Debt!* credit card (p. 108) for each young woman. Fold, glue back-to-back. Laminate.

LESSON MATCH ACTIVITY—*Money Mottos*: Use these mottos to remind young women to take responsibility for their finances. Have young women: (1) Write their money goals on the *Think Before I Spend* bill and place bill in their wallet. (2) Have them place the credit card inside of their wallet, reminding them not to overuse their credit cards.

Fun Idea: Give each young woman a small pad of Post-It-Notes to stick on their money motto card. Tell them that "Prioritized spending is as easy as 1,2,3." Just list the items you want to buy and prioritize them in order of purchase, e.g., buy this one first, this one second, and the other third, always using this method to avoid $ stress.

COLOR FLORAL SYMBOL:
*Color floral symbol on activity and scripture card. File activity in Young Women "Value-able" Journal behind the value tab.

Choice & Accountability (orange poppy)

MIDWEEK ACTIVITIES:

Talk About Financial Pitfalls:
Have a banker, accountant, parent, and a college student talk about financial pitfalls. Do a book review on some books that teach the value of saving money.

Wants and Needs Budget Plan:
Step 1: Have a leader talk about how she budgets her time and money to make things work, to avoid debt, and to live within her means. Talk about the peace that can come into a home between husband and wife if they live within their means.

Step 2: Review books on how to budget.

Step 3: Divide young women into two groups, giving each group some play money. Ask them to figure a typical family budget and show where the money goes. Seeing a budget is believing. Have them start out with an average monthly income amount written on a card. Have them write on separate card their wants and needs, listing each expense on a different card. Have them lay the cards out on the table with the money next to the cards that they have budgeted for in that month's budget. Lay the other cards out also and talk about wants and needs.

Step 4: Talk about living within your means, cutting back and planning ahead, e.g., Christmas, birthdays, school clothes. Give the girls an envelope and suggest they place money in the envelope for things they are saving for. Have them write on the envelope things they want and prioritize these. Note that it helps to window shop without a purse and think about items before buying them.

Think before I spend...

- Do I want it?
- Do I need it?
- Can I do without it?

My Money Goals:

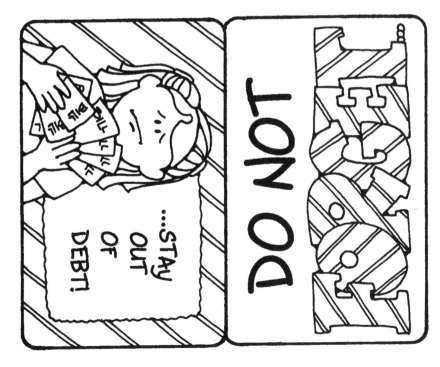

DO NOT

...STAY OUT OF DEBT!

Lesson 47 — Environment: I Will Create an Uplifting Environment
(It's Time for a Change! Diaper Bag)

PREPARATION: Review lesson application (p. 182) in *Young Woman's Manual 2*.

TO MAKE ACTIVITY HANDOUT: *Copy, color, and cut out the *It's Time for a Change! Diaper* bag and cards (p. 110-111) for each young woman. Fold the diaper in the center and glue back-to-back on the bottom left and right sides only, leaving the top open.

LESSON MATCH ACTIVITY—*It's Time for a Change! Diaper Bag*: Help young women think about their present environment and realize that they can change it to be more uplifting by making simple changes. Have young women:
1. Write on the change cards what they want to change about their environment (e.g., their room, their friend's habits or simply change friends, their hobbies, use of their time, personal attitudes, types of entertainment they engage in, media participation, cleanliness).
2. Write on each change card how they will make these changes and slip cards inside the "diaper."

COLOR FLORAL SYMBOL:
*Color floral symbol on activity and scripture card. File activity in Young Women "Value-able" Journal behind the value tab.

Choice & Accountability (orange poppy)

MIDWEEK ACTIVITIES:
Wholesome Home:
Talk about having wholesome pictures, books, and music to create peace and love in the home. Show several of these and have them on display.

Go with Positive Mottos Each Day:
Show traffic signs and talk about actions young women wish to STOP and actions they wish to GO with to make their environment uplifting. They have the power to create happiness each day as they choose positive mottos to live by.

Change Ideas: Young women can write these change ideas on cards to post on their mirror.

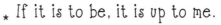

* If it is to be, it is up to me.
* Greet the day with a song.
* Practice smiling three times a day.
* Take my mind off self to focus on others.
* Make my room, home, or workplace clean and inviting.
* Create a house of order, a house of prayer.
* Feed my spirit daily with the scriptures, Church books, magazines, and song.
* Pray daily to invite the Spirit.
* Look for the good in others.
* An interesting person talks to others about their interests.
* Share positive thoughts and feelings.
* Don't attend every argument you're invited to.
* Work ahead so not to lose your head.
* Cook up a storm, but don't let the dishes "reign."

What to change:
_____
_____
_____

How? _____
_____
_____
_____
_____
_____
_____

What to change:
_____
_____
_____

How? _____
_____
_____
_____
_____
_____
_____

What to change:
_____
_____
_____

How? _____
_____
_____
_____
_____

What to change:
_____
_____
_____

How? _____
_____
_____
_____
_____

Lesson 48 Leadership: I Will Increase My Communication Skills

(A Loving or Lazy Leader? Word Find)

PREPARATION: Review chalkboard discussion (p. 184-185) in *Young Woman Manual 2*.

TO MAKE ACTIVITY HANDOUT: *Copy and color *A Loving or Lazy Leader? Word Find* (p. 113) for each young woman.

LESSON MATCH ACTIVITY—*A Loving or Lazy Leader? Word Find*: Ask young women to find the characteristics of a supportive leader and those of an unsupportive or lazy leader.

To Do Word Find:

1. Locate the qualities of a loving leader or a lazy leader scattered throughout the puzzle.

2. Circle the good leader qualities and cross out the lazy leader qualities when you find them. Words can be read from left to right or backwards right to left. The x's indicate blank spaces. *Option:* Instead of circling or crossing out qualities, highlight the loving leader in one color and the lazy leader in another color.

Game Idea: Have young women divide into two teams to compete doing the word find. The first team to finish wins! Give an extra treat to the winning team.

Answers from top to bottom:

Loving Leader: sharing, prepared, prompt, organized, happy, teaches, considerate, calm, sensitive, understanding, concerned, kind, caring, plans, trustworthy, example, listens, forgiving.

Lazy Leader: grumpy, late, idle, insensitive, rude, gossips, tactless, unprepared, forgetful, bossy, neglectful, unorganized, selfish, offensive.

COLOR FLORAL SYMBOL:

*Color floral symbol on activity and scripture card. File activity in Young Women "Value-able" Journal behind the value tab.

Choice & Accountability (orange poppy)

MIDWEEK ACTIVITY:

Smooth Communication Show-and-Tell:

1. Divide young women into several small groups to create a skit. Do some play acting showing various ways of communicating the wrong way (e.g., someone talking and laughing loudly and inappropriately, gossiping, etc.). After a half hour have each group put on their show.

2. Talk about people you know who are patient, soft-spoken, brief, considerate, etc.

3. Have a communications expert come and discuss proper ways of behavior in crowds, one-on-one, small groups, with parents, friends, brothers, and sisters.

4. Read Proverbs 15:1: "A soft answer turneth away wrath." Also Psalm 55:21: "His words were softer than oil."

5. Tell the story of a favorite kindergarten teacher who practically whispered to the children. She never had to speak loud to be heard. They listened intently to every word. When the children asked her to do something they could do for themselves, she simply said, "I'm not your coat hanger." They knew that they must be responsible, even at the early age of five.

A loving or lazy Leader?

Locate the qualities of a loving leader or a lazy leader scattered throughout the puzzle below. Words can be read from left to right or backwards, right to left. X's indicate blank spaces. Circle the good leader qualities and cross out the lazy leader qualities when you find them.

```
G R U M P Y X X X G N I R A H S X X
E T A L X D E R A P E R P X I D X L X E
E X X V I T I S N E S N I E D U X R X X
S P I S S O G X X P R O M P T X X X X X
X X X X O R G A N I Z E D X X A X X X X
X X X S S E L T C A T Y P P A H X X X X
D E R A P E R P N A U X S E H C A E T T
C O N F S I D E R O A T E X M L A C I X
C U N F T E G R O F S E N S A T U V X E
X X G N I D N A T S R E D N U X X X E X
Y S S O B X X X C O N C E R E R N E D X
D N I K X X G N I R A C C X S N A L P X
X X X N E G L E C T F U L X X N X X X X
X X X X X Y H T R O W T S U R T X X X X
U N O R G A N I Z E D E L P M A X X E X
X X S N E T S I L X S E L F I S H X G
O F F E N S I V E F O R G I V I N G
```

Lesson 49	Disabilities: I Will Encourage Others
	(Spread a Little Sunshine Sunny Action Planner)

PREPARATION: Review lesson application (p. 190) in *Young Woman Manual 2.*

TO MAKE ACTIVITY HANDOUT: *Copy, color, and cut out the *Sunny Action Planner* (p. 115) for each young woman. Cut slits in between each sun ray so you have eight flaps.

LESSON MATCH ACTIVITY—*Spread a Little Sunshine Sunny Action Planner:* Ask young women to identify a young woman at school or church who has a disability or special need, or who needs encouragement. Ask young women to reach out and include them in their activities, recognizing their special contributions and helping them participate in school, church, or community activities.

To Use the Sunny Action Planner: Have young women write on each sunray how they plan to spread a little sunshine in the chosen person's life. When they complete their goal (written on the sunray), cut off the sunray or fold it back and tape it to the back of the sun.

Ways to Spread a Little Sunshine: Say hello, offer help, smile, be cheerful, sit by them, invite them places, find ways to help, ask others to help you help, be kind, call them by name, listen, talk about their interests, praise them, recognize their talents.

COLOR FLORAL SYMBOL:
*Color floral symbol on activity and scripture card. File activity in Young Women "Value-able" Journal behind the value tab.

Individual Worth (red rose)

MIDWEEK ACTIVITIES:

Heart Attack:
Surprise someone with a large heart-shaped cookie or box of candy that reads, "Heart Attack!" Attach

several notes with heart stickers or heart-shaped cards with warm encouraging messages. Have young women, leaders, and the bishopric leaders write notes and sign them. Ring the doorbell and run, or stay and visit. Contact the Relief Society compassionate service leader, bishop, or community representatives to find those who need a boost.

Guest Speaker:
Have someone who has a disability come and tell about their life. Young women could visit them in their home, if invited. Speakers could tell how they get along, how they would like to be treated, what they are planning for their life and their dreams for the future.

Spread a little sunshine! - Sunny action Planner

write on each sunray how you plan to spread a little sunshine!

Front cover

My Testimony Grows As I Study the Scriptures

Name:_____

Back cover

My Testimony Grows As I Study the Scriptures

I love ♡ to read the scriptures because they help my testimony to blossom and grow. Blessings come from reading the scriptures and obeying the commandments. "Thou shalt be like a watered garden" (Isaiah 58:11). With the scriptures I can "Bloom Where I'm Planted." The scriptures in this book represent the values taught in the young women lessons. With each scripture card I receive to add to this book, I can do the following: (1) Find the scripture and fill in the missing words. (2) Color the value symbol the value color written at the bottom of the card. Example: Color the poppy (shown right) orange, representing Choice and Accountability. (3) Post scripture cards on my mirror during the week to ponder (Moroni 10:4-5).
4. *Option 1:* Create a book by punching the two hearts (shown right), and tie a bow through holes. *Option 2:* Cut the heart border off and create a card file with A-Z dividers (to file cards by subject) or Young Women value divider tabs.

Inside first page

My Testimony Grows As I Study the Scriptures

Jesus Christ: I Will Draw Close to My Savior

D&C 88:63 "Draw near unto me and I will draw near unto you; _ _ _ _ _ me diligently and ye shall _ _ _ _ _ me; _ _ _ _, and ye shall receive; _ _ _ _ _ _, and it shall be opened unto you."

Young Women Value: Divine Nature (blue morning glory) Lesson 1 Manual 2

♡

My Testimony Grows as I Study the Scriptures

Spiritual Gifts: Spiritual Gifts Help Me Gain Eternal Life

D&C 46:8-9, 26 "Beware lest ye are deceived; and that ye may not be deceived __ __ __ __ ye earnestly the __ __ __ __ gifts, always remembering for what they are __ __ __ __ __; For ... they are given for the benefit of those who __ __ __ __ __ me and keep __ __ __ my commandments . . . and all these gifts come from God, for the __ __ __ __ __ __ __ of the children of God."

♡

Young Women Value: Individual Worth (red rose) Lesson 2 Manual 2

♡

My Testimony Grows as I Study the Scriptures

Kingdom of God: I Will Build God's Kingdom

Matthew 6:31-33 "Take __ __ thought, saying, What shall we __ __ __ __? or, What shall we __ __ __ __ __ __? Or, Wherewithal shall we be __ __ __ __ __ __ __ __? . . . for your heavenly Father knoweth that ye have need of all these things. But seek ye __ __ __ __ __ __ the kingdom of God, and his righteousness; and all these things shall be __ __ __ __ __ unto you."

♡

Young Women Value: Divine Nature (blue morning glory) Lesson 3 Manual 2

♡

My Testimony Grows as I Study the Scriptures

Commandments: Commandments Help Me Fulfill Divine Roles

1 Nephi 3:7 "And it came to pass that I, Nephi said unto my father: I will __ __ and __ __ the things which the __ __ __ __ hath commanded, for I know that the Lord giveth no commandments unto the children of men, save he shall __ __ __ __ __ __ __ a way for them that they may accomplish the thing which he commanded them."

♡

Young Women Value: Divine Nature (blue morning glory) Lesson 4 Manual 2

My Testimony Grows as I Study the Scriptures

Homemaking: Home Can Be a Special Place

D&C 88: 119 "Organize yourselves;
_ _ _ _ _ _ _ every _ _ _ _ _ _ _
thing; and establish a house, even a house of
_ _ _ _ _ _ _, a house of
_ _ _ _ _ _ _, a house of _ _ _ _ _,
a; house of _ _ _ _ _ _ _ _, a house of
_ _ _ _ _, a house of _ _ _ _ _, a house of God."

Young Women Value: Good Works (yellow sunflower) Lesson 5 Manual 2

My Testimony Grows as I Study the Scriptures

Work: Work Is Easier If We All Share

D&C 90:18 "Set in _ _ _ _ _ your houses;
keep slothfulness and uncleanness _ _ _ from
you."
D&C 42:41 "And let all things be done in
_ _ _ _ _ _ _ _ _ _ _ before me."
Moses 3:15 "I the Lord God, took the man, and put
him into the Garden of Eden, to dress it, and to _ _ _ _ it."

Young Women Value: Good Works (yellow sunflower) Lesson 6 Manual 2

My Testimony Grows as I Study the Scriptures

Cooperation: I Will Create Love and Harmony at Home

1 John 2:10-11 "He that loveth his brother
abideth in the _ _ _ _ _ _, and there is none
occasion of stumbling in him. But he that
_ _ _ _ _ _ _ his brother is in darkness, and
walketh in darkness, and knoweth not whether he
goeth, because that darkness hath
_ _ _ _ _ _ _ his eyes."

Young Women Value: Good Works (yellow sunflower) Lesson 7 Manual 2

♡

My Testimony Grows as I Study the Scriptures

Communication: I Will Communicate with My Family

D&C 108:7 "Strengthen your brethren in all your conversation, in all your prayers, in all your exhortations, and in all your _ _ _ _ _ _ _."

1 Peter 3:10-11 "For he that will _ _ _ _ _ life, and see good days, let him refrain his tongue from evil, and his lips that they speak no _ _ _ _ _ _ . . . let him seek peace."

Young Women Value: Good Works (yellow sunflower) Lesson 8 Manual 2

My Testimony Grows as I Study the Scriptures

Peacemaker: I Will Be a Peacemaker in My Home

Proverbs 15:1 "A soft answer turneth away _ _ _ _ _ _: but grievous words stir up _ _ _ _ _ _."

Romans 12:10 "Be _ _ _ _ _ _ _ affectioned one to another with brotherly _ _ _ _ _; in honour preferring one another."

Young Women Value: Good Works (yellow sunflower) Lesson 9 Manual 2

My Testimony Grows as I Study the Scriptures

Priesthood: Priesthood Power Is a Great Blessing

D&C 121:36 "The rights of the priesthood are inseparably connected with the _ _ _ _ _ _ _ of heaven, and . . . the powers of heaven cannot be controlled nor handled only upon the principles of _ _ _ _ _ _ _ _ _ _ _ _ _ _ _."

Young Women Value: Divine Nature (blue morning glory) Lesson 10 Manual 2

| My Testimony Grows as I Study the Scriptures |

Bishop Appreciation (Show Thanks by Thanking God)

Alma 7:23 "I would that ye should be
__ __ __ __ __ __, and be submissive and
gentle; easy to be entreated; full of patience and
long-suffering; being temperate in all things; being
diligent in keeping the commandments of God at all
times; asking for whatsoever thing ye stand in need, both spiritual
and temporal always returning __ __ __ __ __ __ unto God for
whatsoever things ye do receive."

Young Women Value: Good Works (yellow sunflower) Lesson 11 Manual 2

| My Testimony Grows as I Study the Scriptures |

Blessing from Heavenly Father (Lehi Promised Son Joseph)

2 Nephi 3:2-3 "May the Lord consecrate also unto thee
this __ __ __ __ __, which is a most precious land, for thine
inheritance and the inheritance of thy seed with thy
brethren, for thy __ __ __ __ __ __ __ __ forever, if it
so be that ye shall __ __ __ __ the
__ __ __ __ __ __ __ __ __ __ __ __ of the Holy One of Israel. And
now, Joseph, my last-born, whom I have brought out of the wilderness of
mine afflictions, may the Lord bless thee __ __ __ __ __ __ __, for thy
seed shall not utterly be destroyed."

Young Women Value: Individual Worth (red rose) Lesson 12 Manual 2

| My Testimony Grows as I Study the Scriptures |

Patriarchal Blessing Will Guide My Life

Abraham 2:9-11 "I will make thee a great nation, and I
will __ __ __ __ __ thee above measure, and make thy
name great among all nations, and thou shalt be a blessing
unto thy __ __ __ __ after thee, that in their hands
they shall bear this ministry and Priesthood unto all
nations; And I will bless them through thy name; for as
many as receive this Gospel shall be called after thy name, and shall be
accounted thy seed, and shall rise up and bless thee, as their father . . .
right shall continue in thee and in thy seed . . . which are the blessings of
salvation, even of __ __ __ __ eternal."

Young Women Value: Individual Worth (red rose) Lesson 13 Manual 2

My Testimony Grows as I Study the Scriptures

The Temple Brings Blessings

D&C 138:47-48 "The Prophet Elijah was to plant in the hearts of the children the
_ _ _ _ _ _ _ _ _ made to their fathers, Foreshadowing the great work to be done in the temples of the Lord in the dispensation of the fulness of times, for the redemption of the _ _ _ _ _, and the _ _ _ _ _ _ _ _ of the children to their parents, lest the whole earth be smitten with a curse and utterly wasted at _ _ _ coming."

Young Women Value: Integrity (purple pansy) Lesson 14 Manual 2

My Testimony Grows as I Study the Scriptures

Temple Marriage: I Will Prepare for Temple Marriage

D&C 132:19 "If a man marry a wife by my word, which is my _ _ _, and by the new and everlasting covenant, and it is _ _ _ _ _ _ _ unto them by the Holy Spirit of _ _ _ _ _ _ _ _, by him who is appointed this power and the keys of this priesthood . . . ye shall come forth in the first resurrection, and if it be after the first resurrection, in the next resurrection; and shall inherit _ _ _ _ _ _ _, kingdoms, principalities, and powers, dominions . . . (etc.)."

Young Women Value: Divine Nature (blue morning glory) Lesson 15 Manual 2

My Testimony Grows as I Study the Scriptures

Journals: I Will Record My Personal History

Alma 37:8 "These things should be _ _ _ _ _ _ _ _ _ _; for behold, they have _ _ _ _ _ _ _ _ _ the _ _ _ _ _ _ of this people, yea, and convinced many of the _ _ _ _ _ _ of their ways, and brought them to the knowledge of their _ _ _ unto the salvation of their souls."

Young Women Value: Good Works (yellow sunflower) Lesson 16 Manual 2

My Testimony Grows as I Study the Scriptures

Family History: I Will Keep Family History Records

D&C 128:18 "The earth will be smitten with
a __ __ __ __ __ __ unless there is a welding
__ __ __ __ __ of some kind or other between
the fathers and the children . . . It is the baptism
for the dead. For we without them cannot be made
__ __ __ __ __ __ __ __; neither can they without us be made
__ __ __ __ __ __ __ __ . . ."

Young Women Value: Individual Worth (red rose) Lesson 17 Manual 2

My Testimony Grows as I Study the Scriptures

Traditions: I Will Create Righteous Traditions

D&C 90:24 "__ __ __ __ __ __ __ diligently,
__ __ __ __ __ always, and be believing, and
__ __ __ things shall __ __ __ __ together for
your __ __ __ __, if ye walk uprightly and
remember the covenant wherewith ye have
covenanted one with another."

Young Women Value: Integrity (purple pansy) Lesson 18 Manual 2

My Testimony Grows as I Study the Scriptures

Missionary Work: I Will Prepare to Teach the Gospel

Alma 4:18-20 "[Alma prepared to] go forth among . . .
the people . . ., that he might __ __ __ __ __ __ the
__ __ __ __ of God unto them, to __ __ __ __ them up
in remembrance of their duty, and that he might pull
down, by the word of God, all the __ __ __ __ __ and
craftiness and all the contentions which were among his
people, seeing no way that he might reclaim them save it were in bearing
down in pure testimony against them . . . to the testimony of the word,
according to the spirit of revelation and prophecy."

Young Women Value: Good Works (yellow sunflower) Lesson 19 Manual 2

♡

My Testimony Grows as I Study the Scriptures

Missionary: I Will Share the Gospel

1 Timothy 4:12 "Let no man despise thy youth, but be thou an __ __ __ __ __ __ __ of the believers, in word, in conversation, in charity, in spirit, in faith, in purity."

1 Peter 3:15 "Sanctify the Lord God in your hearts: and be __ __ __ __ __ always to give an __ __ __ __ __ __ to every man that asketh you a reason of hope that is in you with meekness and fear."

Young Women Value: Good Works (yellow sunflower) Lesson 20 Manual 2

My Testimony Grows as I Study the Scriptures

Missionary: I Will Sustain Missionaries Through Letters

D&C 88:80-81 "Be prepared in all things when I shall send you again to __ __ __ __ __ __ __ __ the calling whereunto I have called you, and the mission with which I have commissioned you. Behold, I send you out to __ __ __ __ __ __ __ __ and warn the people, and it becometh every man who hath been warned to __ __ __ __ __ his neighbor."

Young Women Value: Good Works (yellow sunflower) Lesson 21 Manual 2

My Testimony Grows as I Study the Scriptures

I Will Counsel with the Lord in Prayer

Alma 37:37 "Counsel with the Lord in __ __ __ thy doings, and he will __ __ __ __ __ __ thee for __ __ __ __; yea, when thou liest down at night lie down unto the Lord, that he may __ __ __ __ __ __ over you in your sleep; and when thou risest in the morning let thy __ __ __ __ __ be full of thanks unto God; and if ye do these things, ye shall be lifted up at the __ __ __ __ day."

Young Women Value: Divine Nature (blue morning glory) Lesson 22 Manual 2

My Testimony Grows as I Study the Scriptures

Fasting Brings Blessings

Omni 1:26 "Come unto him, and offer your whole souls as an offering unto him, and continue in fasting and prayer, and __ __ __ __ __ __ to the end; and as the Lord liveth ye will be __ __ __ __ __."

Helaman 3:35 "They did fast and pray oft, and did __ __ __ stronger and stronger in their __ __ __ __ __ __ __ __, and firmer and firmer in their __ __ __ __ __ of Christ, unto the filling their souls with __ __ __ and consolation ..."

Young Women Value: Faith (white lily) Lesson 23 Manual 2

My Testimony Grows as I Study the Scriptures

Revelation: I Will Seek Each Day

Moroni 10:4-5 "And when ye shall receive these things, I would exhort you that ye would __ __ __ God, the Eternal Father, in the name of Christ, if these things are not true; and if ye shall ask with a sincere heart, with __ __ __ __ intent, having __ __ __ __ __ __ in Christ, he will manifest the __ __ __ __ __ __ of it unto you, by the power of the Holy Ghost. And by the power of the Holy Ghost ye may __ __ __ __ the truth of all things."

Young Women Value: Divine Nature (blue morning glory) Lesson 24 Manual 2

My Testimony Grows as I Study the Scriptures

Sacrifice: I Will Understand the Meaning of Sacrifice

D&C 64:29-31 "As ye are __ __ __ __ __ __ __, ye are on the Lord's __ __ __ __ __ __ __ __; and whatever ye do according to the will of the Lord is the Lord's business. And he hath set you to __ __ __ __ __ __ __ __ for his saints in these __ __ __ __ days, that they may obtain an inheritance in the land of Zion. And behold, I, the Lord, declare unto you, and my words are __ __ __ __ and shall not fail, that they shall obtain it."

Young Women Value: Good Works (yellow sunflower) Lesson 25 Manual 2

My Testimony Grows as I Study the Scriptures

Sacrament: I Will Choose the Right

Matthew 26:26-28 "And as they were eating, Jesus took __ __ __ __, and blessed it, and brake it, and gave it to the disciples, and said, Take, eat; this is my __ __ __ __. And he took the cup, and gave __ __ __ __ __ __, and gave it to them, saying, Drink ye all of it; For this is my blood of the new testament, which is shed for many for the remission of __ __ __ __."

Young Women Value: Choice & Accountability (orange poppy) Lesson 26 Manual 2

My Testimony Grows as I Study the Scriptures

My Testimony Is Strengthened Through Obedience

John 7:17 "If any man __ __ his __ __ __ __, he shall know of the __ __ __ __ __ __ __ __, whether it be of __ __ __, or whether I speak of myself."

James 1:27 "Pure religion and undefiled before God and the Father is this, To __ __ __ __ __ the fatherless and widows in their affliction, and to __ __ __ __ himself unspotted from the world."

Young Women Value: Faith (white lily) Lesson 27 Manual 2

My Testimony Grows as I Study the Scriptures

Agency: I Have the Freedom to Choose

Moses 7:32 "The Lord said unto Enoch: Behold these thy brethren; they are the workmanship of mine own hands, and I gave unto them their __ __ __ __ __ __ __ __ __, in the day I created them; and in the Garden of Eden, gave I unto man his __ __ __ __ __ __."

Young Women Value: Choice and Accountability (orange poppy) Lesson 28 Manual 2

My Testimony Grows as I Study the Scriptures

Exaltation: I Will Earn the Gift of Eternal Life

Abraham 3:25-26 "We will __ __ __ __ __ __
them herewith, to see if they will __ __ all the
things whatsoever the Lord their God shall
__ __ __ __ __ __ __ __ them; And if they who keep
their first estate shall be __ __ __ __ __ __ upon; and
they who keep __ __ __ their first estate shall not have
__ __ __ __ __ __ in the same kingdom with those who keep their
first estate; and they who keep their second estate shall have
glory added upon their heads for ever and ever."

Young Women Value: Divine Nature (blue morning glory) Lesson 29 Manual 2

My Testimony Grows as I Study the Scriptures

My Testimony Is Strengthened Through Service

D&C 115:4-5 "For thus shall my church be called
in the __ __ __ __ days, even The Church of Jesus
Christ of Latter-day Saints. Verily I say unto all:
Arise and __ __ __ __ __ __ forth, that thy
__ __ __ __ __ __ may be a standard for the nations."

Young Women Value: Faith (white lily) Lesson 30 Manual 2

My Testimony Grows as I Study the Scriptures

Patriotism: I Love My Country

D&C 134:1 "We believe that governments were
instituted of God for the __ __ __ __ __ __ __ __
of man; and that he holds men accountable for their
__ __ __ __ __ in relation to them, both in making
__ __ __ __ __ and administering them, for the good and safety of
society."

Young Women Value: Good Works (yellow sunflower) Lesson 31 Manual 2

| **My Testimony Grows as I Study the Scriptures** |

Life Is Sacred

1 Nephi 17:36 "The Lord hath created the earth that it should be __ __ __ __ __ __ __ __ __ __; and he hath created his children that they should __ __ __ __ __ __ __ __ it."

Young Women Value: Choice and Accountability (orange poppy) Lesson 32 Manual 2

| **My Testimony Grows as I Study the Scriptures** |

Chastity: I Will Honor the Sacred Power of Procreation

Alma 41:10-11 "Do not suppose, because it has been spoken concerning restoration that ye shall be restored from __ __ __ to happiness. Behold, I say unto you, wickedness never was happiness . . . All men that are in a state of nature, or I would say, in a carnal state, are in the gall of bitterness and in the __ __ __ __ __ __ of iniquity; they are without God in the world, and they have gone contrary to the nature of God; therefore, they are in a state contrary to the nature of happiness."

Young Women Value: Choice and Accountability (orange poppy) Lesson 33 Manual 2

| My Testimony Grows as I Study the Scriptures |

Obedience: I Will Hold Fast to the Lord's Standards

Helaman 5:12 "Remember that it is upon the __ __ __ __ __ of our Redeemer, who is Christ, the Son of God, that ye must build your foundation; that when the devil shall send forth is mighty __ __ __ __ __ __, yea, his shafts in the whirlwind, yea, when all his hail and his mighty storm shall __ __ __ __ __ upon you, it shall have __ __ power over you to drag you down to the gulf of misery and endless __ __, because of the rock upon which ye are built, which is a sure foundation, a foundation whereon if men build they cannot __ __ __ __. "

Young Women Value: Choice and Accountability (orange poppy) Lesson 34 Manual 2

♡

My Testimony Grows as I Study the Scriptures

I Will Make Wise Choices

2 Nephi 10:23 "Cheer up your _ _ _ _ _ _ _, and remember that ye are _ _ _ _ _ to act for yourselves—to choose the way of everlasting _ _ _ _ _ _ or the way of eternal _ _ _ _ _."

♡

Young Women Value: Choice & Accountability (orange poppy) Lesson 35 Manual 2

♡

My Testimony Grows as I Study the Scriptures

I Will Be Honest with Myself and Others

D&C 3:7-8 "You should not have feared man more than God. Although men set at naught the counsels of God, and _ _ _ _ _ _ _ _ his words—Yet you should have been faithful; and he would have extended his arm and supported you against all the _ _ _ _ _ _ darts of the adversary and he would have been with you; in every time of _ _ _ _ _ _ _ _."

♡

Young Women Value: Integrity (purple pansy) Lesson 36 Manual 2

♡

My Testimony Grows as I Study the Scriptures

Chastity: I Will Maintain Virtue Through Righteous Living

3 Nephi 13:33 "Seek ye _ _ _ _ _ _ the kingdom of God and his righteousness, and all these things shall be added unto you."

D&C 121:45 "Let _ _ _ _ _ _ _ garnish thy thoughts unceasingly; then shall thy confidence wax _ _ _ _ _ _ _ in the presence of God; and the doctrine of the priesthood shall distil upon thy soul as the dews from heaven."

♡

Young Women Value: Choice & Accountability (orange poppy) Lesson 37 Manual 2

My Testimony Grows as I Study the Scriptures

I Will Maintain My Physical Health To Fulfill My Earthly Mission

D&C 88:124 "Cease to be __ __ __ __; cease to be __ __ __ __ __ __ __ __; cease to find fault one with another; cease to __ __ __ __ __ __ longer than needful; retire to thy __ __ __ early, that ye may not be __ __ __ __ __; arise early, that your bodies and your minds may be invigorated."

Young Women Value: Choice & Accountability (orange poppy) Lesson 38 Manual 2

My Testimony Grows as I Study the Scriptures

Physical Health: I Will Learn How to Prevent Disease

Alma 11:42-44 "Christ shall loose the bands of this temporal death, that all shall be raised from this temporal death. The spirit and the body shall be reunited again in its __ __ __ __ __ __ __ __ form . . . . both the __ __ __ __ __ __ __ and the righteous . . . shall be restored to its perfect frame . . . to be judged according to their works . . ."

Young Women Value: Choice & Accountability (orange poppy) Lesson 39 Manual 2

My Testimony Grows as I Study the Scriptures

Self Mastery: I Will Strengthen My Character

Ether 12:27 "If men come unto me I will __ __ __ __ unto them their weaknesses. I give unto men weaknesses that they may be __ __ __ __ __ __ __; and my grace is sufficient for all men that humble themselves before me; for if they humble themselves before me, and have __ __ __ __ __ in me, then will I make weak things become __ __ __ __ __ __ __ unto them."

Young Women Value: Integrity (purple pansy) Lesson 40 Manual 2

My Testimony Grows as I Study the Scriptures

Optimism: I Will Develop a Cheerful, Optimistic Attitude

Mosiah 2:41 "Consider on the __ __ __ __ __ __ __ __ and __ __ __ __ __ __ state of those that __ __ __ __ __ the commandments of God. For behold, they are __ __ __ __ __ __ __ __ __ in all things, both temporal and spiritual; and if they hold out faithful to the __ __ __ they are received into heaven, that thereby they may __ __ __ __ __ __ with God in a state of never-ending happiness. O remember, remember that these things are true; for the Lord God hath spoken it. "

Young Women Value: Choice and Accountability (orange poppy) Lesson 41 Manual 2

My Testimony Grows as I Study the Scriptures

Gratitude: I Will Express Appreciation

D&C 78:19 "He who __ __ __ __ __ __ __ __ __ __ all things with thankfulness shall be made glorious; and the things of this __ __ __ __ __ shall be __ __ __ __ __ __ unto him, even an hundred fold, yea, __ __ __ __ __."

Young Women Value: Choice & Accountability (orange poppy) Lesson 42 Manual 2

My Testimony Grows as I Study the Scriptures

Management: I Will Use My Time Wisely

1 Timothy 6:17-19 "Charge them that are rich in this world, that they be not high minded, nor trust in uncertain riches, but in the living God, who giveth us richly all things to enjoy; That they do good, that they be rich in good __ __ __ __ __ __, ready to __ __ __ __ __ __ __ __ __ __, willing to communicate; Laying up in store for themselves a good foundation against the time to come, that they may lay hold on __ __ __ __ __ __ __ life."

Young Women Value: Choice & Accountability (orange poppy) Lesson 43 Manual 2

My Testimony Grows as I Study the Scriptures

I Will Develop My Talents

D&C 88:33 "For what doth it __ __ __ __ __ __ a man if a gift is bestowed upon him, and he receive not the gift? Behold, he rejoices __ __ __ in that which is given unto him, neither rejoices in him who is the giver of the __ __ __ __ __."

D&C 60:13 "Thou shalt not __ __ __ __ away thy time, neither shalt thou __ __ __ __ __ thy talent that it may not be __ __ __ __ __."

Young Women Value: Individual Worth (red rose) Lesson 44 Manual 2

My Testimony Grows as I Study the Scriptures

Cultural Arts Participation

D&C 88:118 "Seek ye diligently and __ __ __ __ __ __ one another words of __ __ __ __ __ __ __; yea, seek ye out of the best __ __ __ __ __ __ words of wisdom; seek learning, even by __ __ __ __ __ and also by faith."

Young Women Value: Knowledge (green ivy) Lesson 45 Manual 2

My Testimony Grows as I Study the Scriptures

I Will Learn to Be Financially Responsible

Jacob 2:18-19 "Before ye seek for __ __ __ __ __ __ __, seek ye for the kingdom of God. And after ye have obtained a hope in Christ ye shall obtain __ __ __ __ __ __ __, if ye seek them; and ye will seek them for the intent to do __ __ __ __ — to __ __ __ __ __ __ the naked, and to __ __ __ __ the hungry, and to liberate the captive, and to administer relief to the __ __ __ __ and the afflicted."

Young Women Value: Choice and Accountability (orange poppy) Lesson 46 Manual 2

| My Testimony Grows as I Study the Scriptures |

I Will Create an Uplifting Environment

Article of Faith 13
"If there is anything _ _ _ _ _ _ _ _ _,
lovely, or of good report or praiseworthy, we
_ _ _ _ after these things."

Philippians 4:8
"Whatsoever things are true, . . . honest, . . . just, . . . pure, . . .
lovely, . . . good report; if there be any virtue, and if there be any
_ _ _ _ _ _ _, think on these things."

Young Women Value: Choice & Accountability (orange poppy) Lesson 47 Manual 2

| My Testimony Grows as I Study the Scriptures |

Leadership: I Will Increase My Communication Skills

D&C 107:99-100 "Let every man learn his
_ _ _ _ _, and to act in the office in which he is
appointed, in all diligence. He that is
_ _ _ _ _ _ _ _ _ shall not be counted
worthy to stand, and he that learns _ _ _ his duty and shows
himself not approved shall not be counted worthy to
_ _ _ _ _ _."

Young Women Value: Choice & Accountability (orange poppy) Lesson 48 Manual 2

| My Testimony Grows as I Study the Scriptures |

Disabilities: I Will Encourage Others

John 13:34-35 "A new commandment that I give
unto you, That ye _ _ _ _ one another; as I
have _ _ _ _ _ you, that ye also _ _ _ _
one another. By this shall all men know that ye are
my _ _ _ _ _ _ _ _ _ _, if ye have
_ _ _ _ one to another."

Young Women Value: Individual Worth (red rose) Lesson 49 Manual 2

My Young Women
Value-able Journal

photo

I will bloom
where I'm planted.

"Thou shalt be like a watered garden."
Isaiah 58:11

How to Place Divider Tabs for Young Women Value-able Journal on the Divider Sheets: (1) Copy tabs on white cardstock. (2) Color floral symbols: Faith (white), Divine Nature (blue), Individual Worth (red), Knowledge (green), Choice and Accountability (orange), Good Works (yellow), and Integrity (purple). (3) Cover with clear contact paper or tape to reinforce tabs. (4) Cut out and fold above word line, i.e., fold above "Faith." (5) Glue or tape tab on divider page in order of the seven values. (6) Also use the tabs for Calendar, Family Home Evening, Friends, Personal Progress, and Notes/Journal.

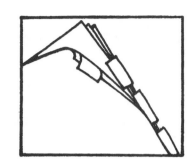

Faith white lily	Divine Nature blue morning glory	Individual Worth red rose
Knowledge green ivy	Choice & Accountability orange poppy	Good Works yellow sunflower
Integrity purple pansy	Calendar	Family Home Evening
Friends	Personal Progress	Notes/Journal

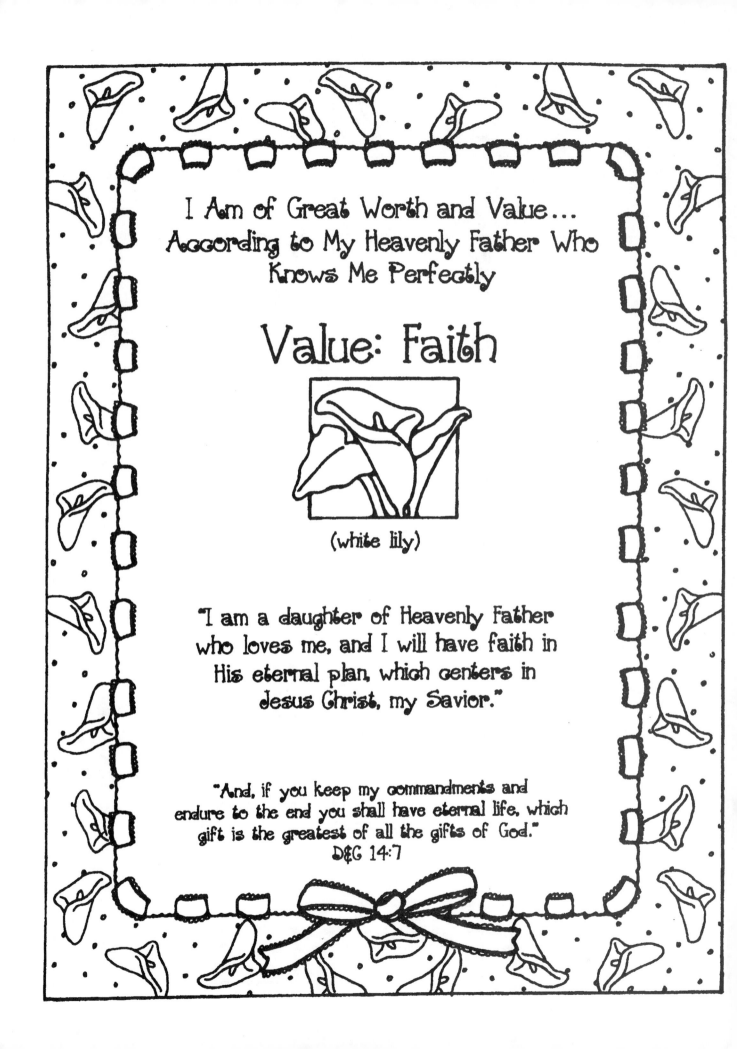

I Am of Great Worth and Value...
According to My Heavenly Father Who
Knows Me Perfectly

Value: Faith

(white lily)

"I am a daughter of Heavenly Father
who loves me, and I will have faith in
His eternal plan, which centers in
Jesus Christ, my Savior."

"And, if you keep my commandments and
endure to the end you shall have eternal life, which
gift is the greatest of all the gifts of God."
D&C 14:7

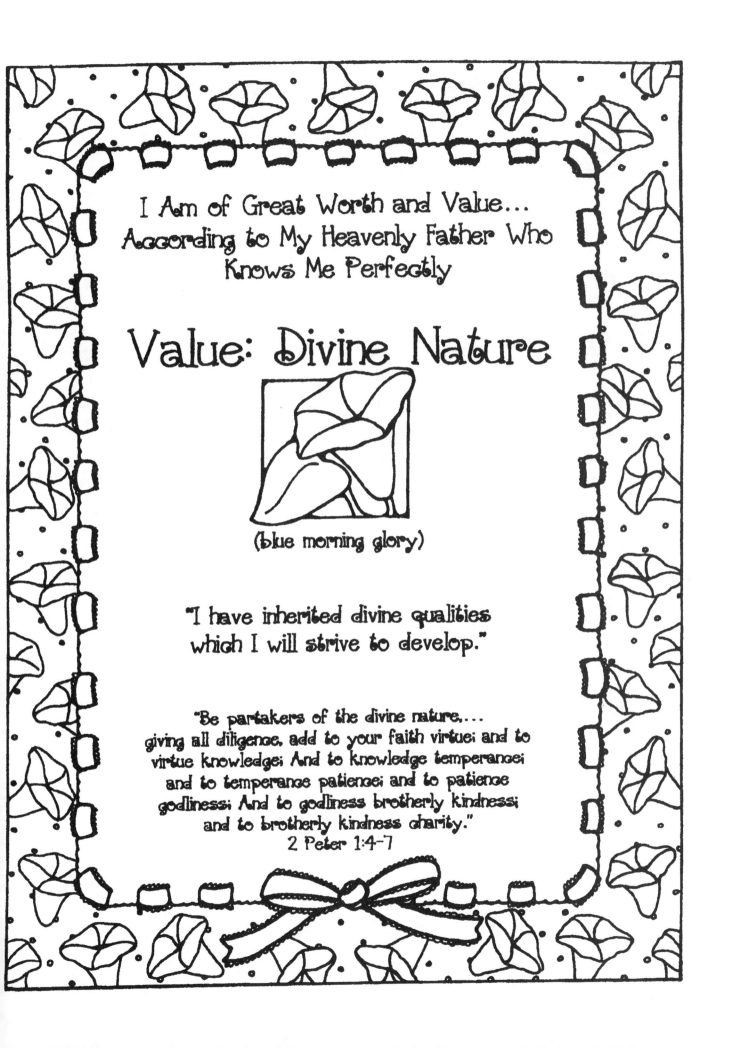

I Am of Great Worth and Value...
According to My Heavenly Father Who
Knows Me Perfectly

Value: Divine Nature

(blue morning glory)

"I have inherited divine qualities
which I will strive to develop."

"Be partakers of the divine nature,...
giving all diligence, add to your faith virtue; and to
virtue knowledge; And to knowledge temperance;
and to temperance patience; and to patience
godliness; And to godliness brotherly kindness;
and to brotherly kindness charity."
2 Peter 1:4-7

I Am of Great Worth and Value...
According to My Heavenly Father Who
Knows Me Perfectly

Value: Individual Worth

(red rose)

"I am of infinite worth with my
own divine mission, which I
will strive to fulfill."

"Remember the worth of souls is
great in the sight of God."
D&C 18:10

I Am of Great Worth and Value...
According to My Heavenly Father Who
Knows Me Perfectly

Value: Knowledge

(green ivy)

"I will continually seek
opportunities for learning
and growth."

"Seek learning, even by study
and also by faith."
D&C 88:118

I Am of Great Worth and Value...
According to My Heavenly Father Who
Knows Me Perfectly

Value: Choice and Accountability

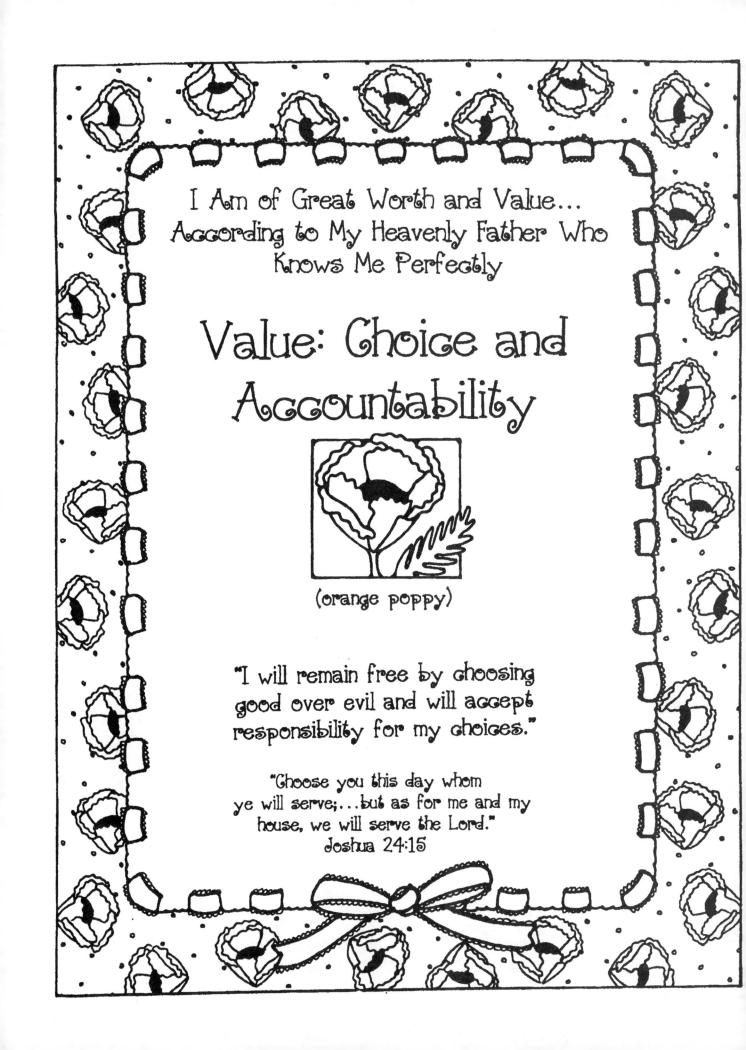

(orange poppy)

"I will remain free by choosing
good over evil and will accept
responsibility for my choices."

"Choose you this day whom
ye will serve;...but as for me and my
house, we will serve the Lord."
Joshua 24:15

I Am of Great Worth and Value...
According to My Heavenly Father Who
Knows Me Perfectly

Value: Good Works

(yellow sunflower)

"I will nurture others and build the
kingdom through righteous service."

"Therefore let your light so shine
before this people, that they may see your good
works and glorify your Father who is in heaven."
3 Nephi 12:16

I Am of Great Worth and Value...
According to My Heavenly Father Who
Knows Me Perfectly

Value: Integrity

(purple pansy)

"I will have the moral courage to
make my actions consistent
with my knowledge of right
and wrong."

"Till I die I will not remove
mine integrity from me."
Job 27:5